Comprehension Strategies for an Integrated Language Arts Classroom

by Dorothy Rubin

Fearon Teacher Aids
A Paramount Communications Company

Dedication

With love to my supportive and understanding husband, Artie,
my precious daughters, Carol and Sharon,
my delightful grandchildren, Jennifer, Andrew, Melissa, and Kelsey,
my charming son-in-law, Seth, and my dear brothers and sister.

Publisher: Virginia L. Murphy
Editor: Lisa Schwimmer
Cover Design: Teena Remer
Inside Illustration and Design: Teena Remer

ISBN 0-86653-912-3

Printed in the United States of America

1.9 8 7 6 5 4 3 2 1

Contents

About This Resource

Comprehension Strategies for an Integrated Language Arts Classroom is intended to be a valuable resource for the classroom teacher, providing a wealth of challenging and stimulating reading comprehension activities for young students. The wide variety of material found in this resource will help the classroom teacher as he or she works with students of all ability levels. *Comprehension Strategies for an Integrated Language Arts Classroom* is published in a format that includes practice pages that are easily reproducible for distribution to the children in your classroom—an important time-saver for you.

The skills and strategies presented in *Comprehension Strategies for an Integrated Language Arts Classroom* deal with reasoning with verbal concepts and word meanings—these are the two major abilities that are the basis for solid reading comprehension. Comprehension involves thinking. As there are various levels in the hierarchy of thinking, so are there various levels of reading comprehension. Higher levels of comprehension would obviously include higher levels of thinking. This book concentrates on the higher-order comprehension skills because these are the strategies often neglected in schools—and all students need help in acquiring these abilities. More and more across the country, teachers are emphasizing the teaching of higher-order comprehension skills and strategies.

This book is based on the premise that primary-grade children can and should be exposed to high-level comprehension skills at their individual literacy levels. As noted educator Jerome Bruner said in his book *The Process of Education* (Cambridge, MA: Harvard University Press, 1963), "Any subject can be taught effectively in some intellectually honest form to any child at any stage of development." While Bruner contends that this is a bold statement, there is little evidence to contradict it—and there is considerable evidence to support it. In the primary grades, children should be learning comprehension skills and strategies concomitantly with decoding, and these skills should be presented in a meaningful context. The material that the children are reading should be interesting and related as closely as possible to what the children are learning. Reading is a thinking act, and unless children comprehend what they are reading, they are not *really* reading.

Whom This Guide Is For

The material in *Comprehension Strategies for an Integrated Language Arts Classroom* is designed for students in the primary grades (K-4), but can be used with older students as well. The emphasis in *Comprehension Strategies for an Integrated Language Arts Classroom* is on engaging children in activities that will help them become good, strategic readers.

Recent studies suggest strongly that "reading skill may not be developed as quickly or as well in the primary grades as is believed," and that "we are just beginning to detect the dire consequences that a poor initial start with reading has on later development." (From

Connie Juel's "Beginning Reading" in *Handbook of Reading Research,* Vol. II, Rebecca Barr, Michael L. Kamil, Peter Mosenthal, and P. David Pearson, eds., New York: Longman, 1991, p. 759.) *Comprehension Strategies for an Integrated Language Arts Classroom* can help ensure primary-grade teachers that their students are learning the comprehension skills and strategies they need to become good readers and ultimately succeed in school.

If you are a teacher with highly able children, you will find *Comprehension Strategies for an Integrated Language Arts Classroom* a helpful teaching tool as well. The material provides the kind of challenges in higher-order thinking that gifted children need and enjoy.

The Organization

Comprehension Strategies for an Integrated Language Arts Classroom is organized into the following three sections:

Section One: Selected Reading and Thinking Skills

Section Two: Vocabulary Expansion Skills

Section Three: Fun with Words: Word Riddles and Word Puzzles

Sections One and Two contain fourteen skill and strategy areas for a total of 125 practice exercises. Each skill and strategy area includes accompanying teacher material and student practice sheets. The teacher material precedes the practices and contains the following:

Explanation
Teaching Strategies in Action
     Sample Practices
     Modeling Strategy
Learning Objective
Directions for Student Practices
Extensions
Assessment Tool Progress Report

The Assessment Tool Progress Report, as well as the practice exercises, can be reproduced by the classroom teacher. The teacher material offers suggestions for record keeping and can be especially helpful for classroom portfolios.

The student practices for each skill strategy are graduated in levels of difficulty. The beginning exercises are easier, the following are more difficult. Teachers can, therefore, choose appropriate exercises based on the ability level of each student. The progression from easier to more difficult allows each student initial success in working with the material. Clear and understandable directions are provided for each exercise. For some of the exercises, when necessary, special teacher instructions are provided.

Section Three, "Fun with Words," contains 88 word riddles and word puzzles your students will find interesting, enjoyable, and challenging.

Some Suggestions for Use

Comprehension Strategies for an Integrated Language Arts Classroom can be used in various settings and with a variety of students. This resource can be used in a whole-language classroom—or in any classroom (see "What Is an Integrated Language Arts Classroom?" on page 11). Regardless of the program you currently embrace, *Comprehension Strategies for an Integrated Language Arts Classroom* can help you stay aware of your students' individual differences as you continue to learn more about their reading behaviors.

I encourage you to be continuously assessing your children's reading behavior. Gain information about your students' reading behavior using observation and classroom portfolios, as well as, when appropriate, informal and formal diagnostic measures. You can then use this data to either reinforce, supplement, enrich, or develop skill and strategy areas using material from *Comprehension Strategies for an Integrated Language Arts Classroom*.

The materials in each section of this resource can be used in working with individual children, in small groups, or with the entire class.

What Is an Integrated Language Arts Classroom?

An integrated language arts classroom is one in which the best of whole-language practices and a sequential development of skills are fully integrated. In such a classroom, teachers integrate various aspects of the whole-language movement with different programs to achieve a balanced, eclectic approach that is also practical.

In an integrated language arts classroom, the emphasis is on helping students improve their higher-order thinking skills and comprehension abilities, as well as fostering a love of books.

What Is the Role of the Teacher in an Integrated Language Arts Classroom?

Teachers are the key to the success of any program. Good teachers are aware of the individual differences of students in their classrooms, the interrelatedness of reading with the other language arts, and they understand their role in the teaching of reading.

In an integrated language arts classroom, teachers are the key decision-makers. They determine which materials, practices, skills, and strategies to use in their classrooms based on the individual needs of their students. In an integrated language arts classroom, teachers use trade books, children's writings, newspapers, textbooks, and all other appropriate materials as springboards for children's listening, speaking, reading, and writing.

Scenario: Ms. Hall in Action

Ms. Hall has been teaching reading to young children for over thirty years. She started teaching right out of college and prides herself on keeping abreast of her field. She especially enjoys noticing new trends and comparing them to the approaches she has used in her teaching over the years.

Ms. Hall loves to teach. This is evident in her relationships with her students and by what takes place in her classroom. When you ask Ms. Hall what excites her about teaching, she says "Nothing can outdo the joy of knowing that you have taken children by the hand and helped them to unlock the mystery of reading. What can be more exciting than seeing veiled eyes suddenly sparkle with a gleam that says 'I understand'? How many other careers are there that can bring such rewards each day?"

Ms. Hall has a group of twenty-five first graders in her classroom. She is fortunate to have a teacher's aide with whom she works very closely. At the beginning of every year, Ms. Hall spends the first few weeks getting to know her students and establishing a nonthreatening environment in her classroom where creativity can flourish and students are not afraid to be risk-takers.

During the first few weeks of school, Ms. Hall helps her students establish certain routines and procedures so they can live together in harmony. She encourages suggestions from the children. She also trains her teacher's aide to be more than a clerk or assistant. She helps her teacher's aide gain the strategies and skills she needs to help with direct instruction.

Ms. Hall engages her students in many activities in an attempt to gain as much information about her students as she can gather. She also establishes a classroom portfolio system where each child has a folder and in this folder the child stores samples of his or her work-in-progress.

Ms. Hall combines the data from her students' folders with observation and informal and formal tests to organize a program for her students. She knows all her students need to have many, many opportunities to read and write, positive feedback, direct instruction based on their needs, encouragement, and lots of on-task activities. During the school day, Ms. Hall works with the whole class, with individual children, and with small groups of students.

Ms. Hall uses a combination of soft-cover trade books and other reading materials and various approaches to help her students get the most from their reading. Whether she is using a basal reader or a trade book, she employs a directed or guided reading and thinking activity. She also uses the children's experiences to develop language experience stories that they write and read together.

If you were to enter Ms. Hall's first-grade classroom a few months into the school year, you would be greatly impressed with her students' activities. Let's spend part of a day with Ms. Hall in her integrated language arts classroom.

Ms. Hall begins each day with a special poem that she shares with the class. Today she is reading aloud Amy Lowell's poem "City of Falling Leaves"—because today is a windy fall day and leaves of all colors are falling to the ground. After she reads the poem, she engages the children in a lively discussion about fall and falling leaves. Ms. Hall asks the children whether all trees lose their leaves in the fall. "When you go home today," she says, "check to see if there are any trees that still have their leaves. We'll talk about these tomorrow."

Just then a child raises his hand and says that he has lived in another part of the world where trees do not lose their leaves in the fall. He also says that the weather where he used to live almost never changes. Ms. Hall goes to the globe and points to the country where Stephan once lived before he and his family came to the United States. Ms. Hall tells the children that she spoke to Stephan and his mother and that next week Stephan's mother will come to school to talk about Stephan's homeland.

Ms. Hall says "Stephan and his mother are coming to school to talk about the country Stephan and his family once lived in. I though it would be a good idea if we learned something about the country first, so I went to the library and took out some books that have stories about the country Stephan is from. Then we can come up with some questions to ask Stephan and his mother. What do you think it would be like to live in a country that almost always has the same weather? Would it change your life? We'll talk about the questions later today."

Ms. Hall next invites her students to help in the general planning of the day's activities. This is what the class schedule looks like:

Reading groups
Reading aloud to children
Writing stories
Fun with words
Math (working with money—setting up a grocery store)
Lunch
Writing stories
Social studies unit
Storytelling
Creative drama
Special activities
Television reviews

Ms. Hall thanks her students for their help. She then calls a group of students to an area of the room for a small-group instructional unit. (While Ms. Hall is working with the group of students, her teacher's aide is seated in another part of the room surrounded by the rest of the children. The teacher's aide is reading aloud to the other students. She encourages predictions about what she is reading and asks questions before, during, and after.)

Ms. Hall shows her small group of children a small nest with a little cloth hen sitting inside it. Ms. Hall asks the children where they think they might find chickens. A discussion ensues about farms and the kinds of animals children would find there. Ms. Hall asks if the children know what a female chicken is called. When a child says "A hen," Ms. Hall says "Good," and prints the word *hen* on the chalkboard. She then has the children generate a number of words using the *en* word family. First she has them change the initial consonant to form new words. Then she has them change the final consonant. Ms. Hall puts each new word in a sentence. Ms. Hall asks the children for some other word families they have worked with before.

Ms. Hall then prints the following words on the board.

flour	wheat
bread	grain
mill	plant

After Ms. Hall helps the children gain the vocabulary words, she helps the children place each new word in a sentence. She then tells the children they will be reading a story about a little red hen who has three friends. Ms. Hall explains that at the end of the story, the children will find out what kind of friends the little red hen has.

As the children read, Ms. Hall observes the children's reading behavior. Each time the children finish reading a section silently, she asks them to answer some questions. For example, Ms. Hall asks the children what they think the little red hen will do with the wheat. She asks why the little red hen's wheat grew so well. Then she asks the children to find the clues in the story that help them answer these questions and to read the questions aloud.

Throughout the story, Ms. Hall sets purposes for the silent and oral reading and has children make predictions about what they are reading. Before the children come to the end of the story, Ms. Hall asks the children to think about how they would end the story. She writes the children's predictions on paper. Ms. Hall then has the children read the final page in the book to find out what really happens. She then has the children compare their endings with the story's ending. The amount of time Ms. Hall spends on this lesson is based on the attention span and ability levels of the children.

After all the children have returned to their seats, Ms. Hall and the teacher's aide play a game of "Simon Says" with the children. They have a short recess and then Ms. Hall calls the next group to the reading table while the teacher's aide reads aloud to the other group.

Strategies to Help Children Build Their Comprehension Ability

The emphasis in this book is on providing direct instruction to the children. *Direct instruction* is instruction guided by a teacher who uses various strategies or techniques to help children comprehend what they are reading. There are a number of strategies teachers can use to teach reading directly. The strategies that teachers use should not be affected by the kinds of materials they use. In other words, one teacher may embrace whole language and use only trade books in his or her class, while another might use a basal reader. Both teachers can employ similar strategies to help students gain needed concepts. As stated previously, this text advocates a mix of materials, beliefs, and strategies.

Special Note:

A *strategy* is a systematic plan for achieving a specific objective or result. A *reading strategy* is the action or actions that a teacher takes to help children get meaning from text.

Interactive Instruction

In interactive instruction, the teacher intervenes at optimal times to improve classroom instruction. The teacher determines when to intervene and what materials and strategies to use to achieve the desired learning for the readers with whom she or he is working.

Modeling Instruction

Modeling instruction requires teachers to think out loud. That is, teachers verbalize their thoughts to help students "see" an appropriate strategy or reading behavior. This is an exceptionally effective strategy because it helps students gain insight into the kind of thinking involved in reading comprehension and helps children recognize that reading comprehension is analogous to problem solving.

Interactive instruction combined with modeling and knowledge of questioning techniques at various levels is very effective in helping students find meaning in what they are reading.

Scenario: Ms. Hall Uses a Modeling Strategy with Her Class of First Graders

Ms. Hall and seven children are working together at the reading table. They have been reading the story "The Hare and the Tortoise." Ms. Hall has discussed with the children what a hare and a tortoise are and she has shown the children pictures of both and talked about which animal they would expect to move faster and why. She has gone over all new or unfamiliar words in the story with the children, and before they began to read the story, she had asked the children to make predictions about who they thought would win the race.

Today Ms. Hall has asked the children to do something a little different. They are going to be detectives. After discussing what a detective does, Ms. Hall asks the children to look for clues in the story to show why the hare lost the race.

She rereads the story with the children before she shows them how to find story clues. Then she says "While I am reading the first two pages of the story, I see something that tells me the rabbit is very sure of himself. I think to myself that this will probably get him into trouble. Hare said 'Rabbits run fast as the wind.' I don't think he took Tortoise very seriously. Hare feels it's silly to think that Tortoise could possibly win. Because of this, Hare feels he can take it easy. Now, everyone look at the next page. Are there any clues there that show us that the hare could lose the race?"

Ms. Hall calls on different children and elicits from them the reasons for their choices. When they have finished giving all their clues, Ms. Hall asks the children if they have ever heard the saying "Slow and steady wins the race." She asks the children to think about what this means. Later, she says, they will discuss this.

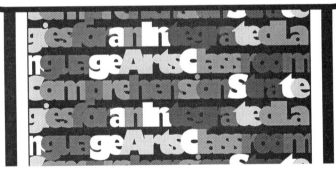

Section One

Selected Reading and Thinking Skills

Questioning Strategies to Enhance Comprehension Ability

All children need help in developing higher-order reading comprehension ability. And asking only literal-type comprehension questions that demand a simple convergent answer won't develop these important higher-order skills.

Much of what has gone on in the past in our schools has been at the literal comprehension level. Teachers in the past often asked questions that required only a literal response. This started to change when the teaching of higher-order comprehension skills was encouraged.

Rather than ask a question that calls for a literal response, more and more teachers are learning to ask questions that call for higher levels of thinking—even as early as kindergarten and first grade. For example, the children have looked at a picture in which children are dressed in snow pants, jackets, hats, mittens, and so on. The teacher can then ask the following questions:

1. What kind of a day is it?
2. Where are the children going?

As children progress to higher levels of thinking, they should be confronted with more complex interpretation or inference problems—according to their individual developmental levels.

Critical reading skills are essential to being a good reader. Teachers can use primary graders' love of fairy tales to begin to develop some critical reading skills. For example, after the children have read "Little Red Riding Hood," the teacher can ask questions like the following:

1. Should Little Red Riding Hood have listened to her mother and not spoken to a stranger? Explain.
2. Would you help a stranger if your mother told you not to speak to a stranger? Explain.
3. Do you think a wolf can talk? Explain.
4. Do you think that this story is true? Explain.
5. Do you think Little Red Riding Hood made wise choices? Explain.

Creative reading questions are probably the most difficult for teachers to come up with. To help children in this area, teachers need to learn how to ask questions that require divergent rather than convergent answers. A teacher who focuses only on the author's meaning or intent and does not go beyond the text will not be encouraging creative reading. Some questions that stimulate divergent thinking on the part of the reader follow:

1. After reading "Little Red Riding Hood," can you come up with another ending for the story?
2. After reading about John, can you come up with a plan for the kind of vacation he would like?

3. After reading the story about the cat that escaped from the well, can you come up with some ideas as to how he was able to escape?

4. Based on your reading about John and his family, what kind of trip would you plan to make them happy?

With divergent questions, there is no one correct answer.

Following is a short reading selection and examples of four different types of comprehension questions. These are being presented so that the teacher can practice recognizing the different types of questions at the four different levels.

One day in the summer, some of my friends and I decided to go on an overnight hiking trip. We all started out fresh and full of energy. About halfway to our destination, when the sun was almost directly overhead, one-third of my friends decided to return home. The remaining four of us, however, continued on our hike. Our plan was to reach our destination by sunset. About six hours later, as the four of us, exhausted and famished, were slowly edging ourselves in the direction of the setting sun, we saw a sight that astonished us. There, at the camping site, were our friends who had claimed that they were returning home. It seems that they did indeed go home, but only to pick up a car and drive out to the campsite.

The following are four different types of comprehension questions:

Literal comprehension: What season of the year was it in the story?

Interpretation: What time of day was it when some of the hikers decided to return home? How many hikers were there when they first started out on the trip? In what direction were the hikers heading when they saw a sight that astonished them? At approximately what time did the sun set? How long did it take for the hikers to reach their destination?

Critical reading: How do you think the hikers felt when they reached their destination? Do you feel that the hikers who went home did the right thing by driving back to the site rather than hiking? Explain.

Creative reading: What do you think the exhausted hikers did and said when they saw their friends who had supposedly gone home?

Developing Selected Reading and Thinking Skills

Reading comprehension is a complex intellectual process involving a number of abilities. The two major abilities have to do with reasoning with verbal concepts and word meanings. Obviously, comprehension involves thinking. Asking only comprehension questions of a literal type, which demand a simple convergent answer that is explicitly stated in the text, does not contribute to the development of higher-order thinking skills. In this book, the emphasis is mainly on practices that require a higher level of thinking.

At the beginning of the book, some literal comprehension questions are included, because the literal comprehension questions are the easiest to answer. These have been presented at the beginning of the book to ensure the child of some success. The literal comprehension questions are followed by interpretive-type questions and those requiring divergent thinking.

The divergent thinking skill, which is a high-level skill, is usually presented last in most books—or is not presented at all. In this book, the divergent thinking skill is being presented early in the text because students should be encouraged to engage in this type of thinking as early in their school careers as possible. You should feel free to change the order to any sequence that you feel will better suit the needs of your individual students.

The exercises in Section One concern reading and thinking skills that require reasoning with verbal concepts. A brief explanation of the selected reading and thinking skills presented in the section follows. Note that the skills are being presented as they appear in the book, rather than in any hierarchical order.

Strategy 1	Finding Details That Are Directly Stated	To find information that is directly stated; information that is based on recall.
Strategy 2	Drawing Inferences— "Reading Between the Lines"	To gain understanding from information that is not directly stated.
Strategy 3	Cause and Effect	To determine what makes something happen—that is, why it happens (cause) and the result (effect).
Strategy 4	Finding the Main Idea of a Paragraph	To supply the main thought of a paragraph by determining what the topic is and what is special about the topic. All sentences in the paragraph should develop the main idea.
Strategy 5	Finding the Central Idea of a Story	To supply the central thought of a group of paragraphs or a story by determining what the topic is and what is special about the topic. All paragraphs should develop the central idea.
Strategy 6	Using Divergent Thinking	To go beyond what the author has written to come up with new or alternate solutions.
Strategy 7	Following Directions	To read instructions and then carry them out.
Strategy 8	Categorizing	To classify items into a more general group or to determine whether an item belongs in a specific group.
Strategy 9	Completing Word Relationships (Analogies)	To discern relationships between words or ideas.
Strategy 10	Finding Inconsistencies	To supply the correct word by drawing a logical conclusion from a sentence or story material.
Strategy 11	Distinguishing Between Fact and Opinion	To differentiate between information that can be verified and information that cannot be proven.

Strategy 1:
Finding Details That Are Directly Stated

Explanation

Finding details that are directly stated in a story involves finding information that is clearly expressed within the story. It is a literal comprehension skill that is based on the students' recall of the facts in the story.

Finding details that are directly stated is an activity in which children usually do well. Though children generally have little difficulty with literal comprehension skills, they should certainly have practice with them. In order for children to be able to work with inference (see Strategy 2 on page 31), they need to first learn to recognize the difference between information that is directly stated and information that is not directly stated.

Teaching Strategies in Action

Children need to learn that some information is directly stated in a story and some information is not. Teachers can model for the children how they go about finding information that is directly stated.

Example:
"Miguel and Jackie went to the store."

In this sentence, the details are directly stated—both Miguel and Jackie went to the store. Children do not have to guess what is going on in the sentence because the details are directly stated.

Sample Practices

Here are some sample practices that you can use with your students.

1. Janel and Annette had eggs and toast for breakfast.

Question:
What did Janel and Annette have for breakfast?

Answer:
They had eggs and toast for breakfast.

2. Darnell and Rusty were playing pinball. Darnell got more points at the end of the game than Rusty. Darnell won the game.

Question:
What were Darnell and Rusty playing?

Answer:
They were playing pinball.

Question:
Who won the game?

Answer:
Darnell won the game.

Help your students understand that they can get the information they need by reading it in the text. The answers are directly stated in the story.

Modeling Strategy

Here is how Mr. Johnson models for the children how to find information that is directly stated for the following short selection and the questions that follow it.

Lisa has a pretty little white cat named Snowflake. Lisa likes to play with Snowflake. Snowflake drinks milk from a saucer. Lisa takes good care of Snowflake and Snowflake is happy to be Lisa's pet.

Questions:
1. Who has a cat?
2. What size is the cat?
3. What is the cat's name?
4. What color is the cat?
5. What does the cat drink?
6. Out of what does the cat drink?
7. How does the cat feel about being a pet?

Mr. Johnson asks his students to first read the passage. He says he will also read the passage. Mr. Johnson reads aloud the first question. Then he says "I remember that the first sentence says that Lisa has a pretty little white cat named Snowflake. The short story tells me the answer. It is right there in the first sentence. Now, I read the second question. Again, I remember that the answer is right there in the story. It is directly stated. I can go to the story and find the answer." Mr. Johnson does just that. After he answers the question, he goes to the story and reads aloud the answer. Mr. Johnson does the same for another question. He helps his students see that the answer is directly stated in the story.

After Mr. Johnson has modeled for his students how he answers the questions, he has the students answer the rest of the questions. Mr. Johnson has the children answer the questions based on what the children remember and then find the answer in the story. When they have found the answer, he has one child read the answer aloud.

Learning Objective

To find information that is directly stated in a passage or story.

Directions for Student Practices

Use the student practice worksheets on pages 26-30 to help your students acquire, reinforce, and review finding details directly stated in the text. Pick and choose the practices based on the needs and developmental levels of your students. Answers for the student practice pages are on page 298.

When practicing finding details directly stated in the text, have the children read the story and then answer the questions. For those who have difficulty reading, read the story aloud to the children and orally ask them the questions.

Extensions

Picture Postcards

Invite children to create picture postcards. Give each child a large index card and encourage the children to use their imaginations to draw and color the postcards. The postcards can be from Zip and Zap on the moon or the children can write their own postcards to family and friends from the moon, another country, or anywhere else they wish.

Puppets

Invite children to make stick puppets of each of the characters in a favorite story. Then challenge children to use their puppets to act out a scene or tell the class about their character.

Asking Questions

After reading a story together or in small groups, divide the class into pairs and invite children to take turns asking each other questions about the story.

Write a Poem

Review with the children the main characters, setting, and plot of a story. Then invite students to write poems about the story, keeping in mind the important details.

What Would You Like to Know?

Encourage students to write four or five questions they would like to ask the main characters of a favorite story. For more of a challenge, ask students to switch papers with another person and invite students to pretend they are one of the main characters in the story and answer their partners' questions.

Strategy 2:
Drawing Inferences—"Reading Between the Lines"

Explanation

Writers often do not directly state what they mean, but present ideas in a more indirect, roundabout way. That is why inference is called the ability to "read between the lines." Inference is defined as "understanding that is not derived from a direct statement but from an indirect suggestion."

The ability to draw inferences is especially important in reading fiction, but it is also necessary when reading nonfiction. Authors rely on a reader's ability to infer meaning to make their stories more interesting and enjoyable. Mystery writers find inference essential to the suspense in their stories. For example, Sherlock Holmes and Perry Mason mysteries are based on the ability of the characters to uncover clues that are not obvious to others around them.

Question Answer Relationships (QARs) can be very useful in introducing children to inferential reasoning. This process can help children understand better what information is directly stated and what is implied. In the QAR technique, students learn that they not only must consider information that is in the text, but also information they already know. Here are some of the things that you can do to help children recognize the differences between information that is in the story and information that they already have in their heads—that is, information they bring to the story. Present children with a story, such as the following:

> Pete and his brother went to the ball game.
> They were lucky to get tickets for the game.
> They saw many people that they knew.
> At the game, Pete and his brother ate hot dogs.
> They also drank soda.

Then ask the children the following questions:

1. Where did Pete and his brother go? (To the ball game)
2. Where did they see the people? (At the ball game)

Help the children see that the first answer is directly stated in the passage. The first sentence says that Pete and his brother went to the ball game. The answer to the second sentence is not directly stated. The answer to the second question is already in the children's heads because they know from the first sentence that Pete and his brother went to the ball game. Therefore, the children can infer that Pete and his brother saw many people at the ball game from reading the first sentence.

Inference is an important process that authors rely on. Good readers must be alert to the ways that authors encourage inference.

Special Note

Interpretation questions concern answers that are not directly stated in the text but are implied. All questions at the interpretive level are inference questions. Because of this, there is generally confusion concerning the term *inference*. The definition of inference is very broad and includes all of the skills that come under the interpretive level. However, when teachers refer to inference, they are usually referring to the specific skill of "reading between the lines."

Teaching Strategies in Action

To understand text, the reader must be alert and able to detect the clues that the author gives.

> *Example:*
> "Things are always popping and alive when the twins,
> Jason and Scott, are around."

In this sentence, you are given some clues to Jason and Scott's personalities, even though the author has not directly said anything about their personalities. From the statement, you could make the inference that the twins are lively and fun, or maybe even devious or troublesome.

Caution your students not to read more into statements than is intended. Read the following statement.

> *Example:*
> Mary got out of bed and looked out of the window. She saw
> that the ground had some white on it.
>
> Question:
> What season of the year was it?
>
> Answer:
> (a) winter; (b) summer; (c) spring; (d) fall; (e) can't tell.

The answer is "(e) can't tell." Many people choose "(a) winter" for the answer. However, the answer is (e) because the "something white" could be anything; there isn't enough evidence to choose (a). Even if the something white were snow, in some parts of the world, including the United States, it can snow in the spring or fall.

Sample Practices

Here are some sample practices that you can use with your students.

1. Mary looked out of the train window. She saw some leafless trees.

Question:
What season of the year was it? Circle the correct answer and give reasons for your answer.
(a) winter; (b) summer; (c) fall; (d) spring; (e) can't tell

Answer:

(e) can't tell. It could be any season of the year. We do not know in which part of the country or world Mary is traveling. The trees could be leafless as a result of a forest fire, disease, or some other cause.

2. The hikers walked toward the mountain range. Some of the hikers needed to sit down. They were out of breath.

Question:

Why were the hikers out of breath?

Answer:

Because they were tired or because of the high altitude.

Help your students see that the clues are not directly stated in the story, but that they are all there.

Modeling Strategy

Ms. Stein writes a short paragraph with questions on the board. Here it is:

The horses had been out in the desert for a long time. Their manes were covered with dust. The sun beat down on them and they needed something to drink.

Questions:
1. What kind of a day was it?
2. Why did the horses need something to drink?

Ms. Stein says the following:

"Let's read the paragraph together. Now, I'm going to say aloud how I would answer the first question 'What kind of a day was it?' See if you agree. I remember that the last line of the paragraph says that the sun beat down on them, so it must be hot. But I also see that the horse's manes were covered with dust. So it must be a very dry day. I infer or read between the lines that it is a very dry day. Now I read the second question, which is 'Why did the horses need something to drink?' I remember that the horses are in the desert. A desert is usually dry. The last sentence starts with 'the sun beat down on them' so I know it's also hot. The horses are hot and dry which probably makes them thirsty. So I see that the answer to the second question is that the horses need something to drink because they are thirsty."

Ms. Stein then writes another paragraph on the board. Here it is:

The children were hiking toward a forest. The sun was setting behind the trees. When they got to the forest, the children decided to sit down and eat lunch.

Question:

In what direction were the children going?

"Here's what I do to answer this question. First I think what clues help me figure out direction. Let's see, the children are walking toward the forest. The second sentence says the sun was setting behind the trees. I already know that the sun sets in the west. Because the sun is setting behind the trees, the children are going west."

Ms. Stein helps the children see that even though the clues are not directly stated in the story, there is enough information to answer the question.

Learning Objective

To draw inferences or "read between the lines" to find meaning.

Directions for Student Practices

Use the student practices on pages 37-46 to help your students acquire, reinforce, and review drawing inferences. Pick and choose the practices based on the needs and developmental levels of your students. Answers for the student practice pages are on pages 299-300.

When practicing drawing inferences, have the children read the story and then answer the questions. For those who have difficulty reading, read the story aloud to the children and ask them to respond to the questions orally.

Extensions

Characterization

Have each student choose a character from a favorite story and describe one thing about that character. Ask for explanations. Then invite each student to cover a box with paper. On one side, he or she can draw a picture of the chosen character. On the remaining sides of the box, he or she can give written or picture examples of actions in the story that describe the character.

Postcards and Letters

Encourage each student to write a postcard or letter to a character in a favorite story. Invite students to write about an experience that they had that was similar to something that happened in the story. Encourage children to share their postcards and letters with the class or display the postcards and letters in the classroom.

Making Dioramas

Invite children to create dioramas of the setting based on information given in a favorite story. Children can make a classroom diorama or you may want to divide the class into small groups and invite each group to make a diorama. Encourage children to display their dioramas as well as explain what is going on in each.

Living On the Moon

Invite children to write a story about what they think it would be like to live on the moon. Invite children to think about what kinds of foods they would eat on the moon. Ask children if there are any trees, what the Earth looks like from the moon, and so on. Encourage children to be creative.

Student's Name _____

Assessment Tool Progress Report

Progress

Improvement

Comments

Comprehension Strategies for an Integrated Language Arts Classroom © 1994 Fearon Teacher Aids

Practice 1

This is a make-believe story about an imaginary cat and rat who live on the moon.

Imagine that on the moon, all the food is grown inside a very large house. Zip and Zap, a cat and rat who live on the moon, like to watch the food grow. The food is grown inside the house because there is no air or water outside. The food is grown in a special place and in a special way. Zip and Zap use the same water that the first rats and cats brought to the moon many years ago.

1. Have the cats and rats lived on the moon forever? Explain. _____

_____

2. Why is water reused? _____

3. What are two things that are very precious on the moon? _____

_____

4. What do plants need in order to grow? _____

_____

Name _____

Practice 2

This is a make-believe story about an imaginary cat and rat who live on the moon.

Zip and Zap love to ride in space. Their school goes on a space trip every month. Zip and Zap wear their space clothes and their air masks in the spaceship. All the other moon cats and rats wear them, too. Zip and Zap want to be spaceship pilots. They want to pilot the same spaceship that brought Zip and Zap to the moon a few years ago. The spaceship has its own landing place. It is well taken care of by special cats and rats. Zip and Zap are happy that they can ride in the spaceship.

1. Is there air in the spaceship? Explain. _____

_____

2. Were Zip and Zap born on the moon? Explain._____

_____

3. Is the spaceship important to the moon cats and rats? Explain. _____

_____

4. Is travel an important part of school? Explain._____

_____

_____

Comprehension Strategies for an Integrated Language Arts Classroom © 1994 Fearon Teacher Aids

Name _____

Practice 3

This is a make-believe story about an imaginary cat and rat who live on the moon.

Zip, the cat, and Zap, the rat, wear special clothing on the moon. They must wear this special clothing whenever they go outside. If they did not wear the special clothing, they would not be able to breathe. They also might float away. One day, while they were playing tag inside, Zip was running after Zap. Zap ran outside and jumped up and down. Zip ran outside, too. Zip jumped up, but didn't come down. Zap turned around. When he did, he saw Zip floating away! "Oh, no!" screamed Zap. "Come back! Come back!" But Zip just floated away.

1. Who was wearing special outdoor clothing? How do you know? _____

   _____

   _____

2. Why did Zip float away? _____

   _____

3. What do you think happened to Zip? _____

   _____

4. Did Zip think carefully before he ran outside? Explain. _____

   _____

Name _____

Practice 4

Directions: Read the make-believe story about Zip and Zap, an imaginary cat and rat who live on the moon. Draw a picture of who saved Zip. Or, write or state 5 things about the person or animal who saved Zip. Give clues from the story to support your thinking.

Zip knew that he was in trouble. He floated and floated higher and higher. When he looked down, he couldn't see Zap at all. Zip was frightened. Whenever Zip was frightened, he would close his eyes. All of a sudden, he felt something grab him. He opened his eyes, but he couldn't see anything. He knew that he had stopped floating, but he didn't know where he was. Just then he heard a booming voice. It was so loud that he thought his ears would burst. "Ho, ho, ho, a suitless wonder," the voice said. Zip heard the voice, but still couldn't see where it was coming from. "Well, you're safe now," said the voice. The next thing Zip knew, he was inside the door of his house. Zip was happy to be home. Zap was happy to have Zip home, too.

Name _____

Practice 5

Directions: Read the make-believe story about Zip and Zap, an imaginary cat and rat who live on the moon. Then read each of the sentences below the story. For each of the sentences, see if there is enough information in the story to write *true* or *false*. If there is not enough information, write *can't tell.*

Zip and Zap go to school when it is dark outside. Darkness lasts for 14 Earth days. Daylight lasts for 14 Earth days, too. Zip and Zap do lots of things in school. They learn to read and write. They even have their own robot who helps them. The robot can answer any questions that Zip and Zap might have. They keep their robot busy. Zip and Zap enjoy learning about the Earth and other planets. They like school very much.

1. Zip and Zap go to school for 14 Earth days in a row.   _____

2. One moon day lasts for 28 Earth days.   _____

3. Zip and Zap sleep for 14 days in a row.   _____

4. Zip and Zap ask their robot lots of questions.   _____

5. Zip and Zap do not want to go to school.   _____

6. Zip and Zap have lots of tests in school.   _____

7. Zip and Zap get good grades in school.   _____

8. Zip and Zap's robot can do lots of things.   _____

9. Zip and Zap are interested in geography.   _____

10. Zip and Zap do not have a teacher.   _____

Practice 6

Directions: Read the story. Read each of the sentences below the story. For each of the sentences, see if there is enough information in the story to write *true* or *false*. If there is not enough information, write *can't tell*.

> I would like to play outside today. My mother says I have to wear my snowsuit, hat, and mittens. I am going to build a fort and make a snowman. I see Lucy ice-skating on the pond. I want to play with her.

1. The person in the story is a boy.   _____

2. There is snow on the ground.   _____

3. It is cold outside.   _____

4. The pond is frozen.   _____

5. The person in the story wants to play alone.   _____

Comprehension Strategies for an Integrated Language Arts Classroom © 1994 Fearon Teacher Aids

Name _____

Practice 7

Directions: Read the story. Then read each of the sentences below the story. For each of the sentences, see if there is enough information in the story to write *true* or *false*. If there is not enough information, write *can't tell*.

John and Jim became friends in kindergarten. When Jim came to school the first day, he was frightened and began to cry. John saw Jim crying. He said "Come sit by me," and took Jim's hand. John led Jim to his table and Jim stopped crying. From then on, whenever you saw John, you would know that Jim was close by. The next year of school though, something happened. Whenever you saw John, Jim was not with him.

1. John and Jim are about the same age. _____

2. John and Jim have been friends for 10 years. _____

3. Jim likes broccoli. _____

4. John will be a leader when he grows up. _____

5. John and Jim had a fight. _____

6. Jim moved away. _____

7. John was kind to Jim in kindergarten. _____

8. John and Jim were close friends in kindergarten. _____

9. John and Jim have been friends for about four years. _____

10. John and Jim knew each other before kindergarten. _____

Practice 8

Directions: Read the story. Then read each of the sentences below the story. For each of the sentences, see if there is enough information in the story to write *true* or *false*. If there is not enough information, write *can't tell*.

> The school picnic is tomorrow and all the children can hardly wait. The parents cooked and baked lots of things for the picnic. There are many games to play at the picnic and the teachers and parents play the games, too. Every year, the picnic begins when the sun is almost directly overhead. At the end of the picnic, everyone stands in front of the school building and watches the sun slowly set behind the school building. Then everyone slowly drags himself or herself home.

1. The children are excited about the school picnic.   _____

2. Parents come to the school picnic.   _____

3. At the end of the school picnic, everyone is tired.   _____

4. The school picnic starts about noon.   _____

5. The school picnic takes place on a school day.   _____

6. The teachers play against the parents in the games.   _____

7. The front of the school building faces west.   _____

8. Prizes are given out at the picnic.   _____

9. If it rains, the picnic will be held on another day.   _____

10. The picnic has always been held on a sunny day.   _____

Comprehension Strategies for an Integrated Language Arts Classroom © 1994 Fearon Teacher Aids

Name _____

Practice 9

Directions: Read the story. Read each of the sentences below the story. For each of the sentences, see if there is enough information in the story to write *true* or *false*. If there is not enough information, write *can't tell*.

Three turtles were sitting on a log. The first turtle turned to the other two and said "This is my log! You have to get off." The other two turtles looked at each other and slowly crawled onto another nearby log.

The two turtles spent the day sunning themselves and chatting about the weather. The first turtle sat all by himself with no other turtles to talk to. Soon the first turtle slowly made his way over to the other two turtles. He crawled up beside them on their new log and sat quietly. The other two turtles turned to him and said "Welcome! Would you like to sun yourself with us on our log?" The first turtle said "Yes, thank you." The three turtles spent the rest of the day sunning themselves and chatting about the weather.

1. This is a true story.   _____

2. It was a sunny day.   _____

3. The first turtle liked to share.   _____

4. The first turtle got lonely.   _____

5. All three turtles were males.   _____

6. The turtles were all very old.   _____

7. The two other turtles were kind.   _____

8. It is springtime in the story.   _____

Practice 10

Directions: Read the story. Then answer the questions that follow the story.

Once there was a rich and wise man. He had become rich by working hard. This man lived in a small town and the people in the town wanted to be rich, too. But they didn't like to work very hard. One day, the rich man put a large, dirty box in the middle of the road and then hid behind a bush.

First a farmer came by. The farmer saw the large, dirty box. He did not pick it up or move it out of the way. He left it where it was. Next a miller came by. He, too, just walked around the box. Soon a milkmaid came by. She, too, just walked around the box. Many more people came by. They all walked around the box. At the end of the day, a young boy came by. He had been taking care of sheep all day. When he saw the large, dirty box, he picked it up and moved it out of the way. He didn't want anyone to trip on it. Just as the boy was walking away, he noticed something on the ground. It was where the large, dirty box had been. The something on the ground was a bag of gold.

1. What can you say about the people in the story who walked around the box?

_____

2. Why did the rich man hide behind the bush? _____

_____

3. What can you say about the boy in the story? _____

_____

4. Where had the gold been placed?_____

5. Who had left the gold?_____

6. Why was the gold left? _____

_____

Comprehension Strategies for an Integrated Language Arts Classroom © 1994 Fearon Teacher Aids

Strategy 3:
Cause and Effect

Explanation

Children need to understand why things happen to get the most from what they are reading. A *cause* makes something happen. It is why something takes place. An *effect* is the result of the cause. It is what happens. Writers often state the cause and then provide the result(s) or effect(s). Other times writers state the effect and then give the cause(s).

Teaching Strategies in Action

Explain to the children that when they read, they should ask themselves *what happened* and *why*. These two questions are probably the most effective ways of figuring out cause and effect relationships.

Teachers can also tell students to be on the lookout for the word *because*, which is often a signal that tells us why something happened. It signals a cause or causes.

Examples:
When the clown did funny tricks, Chris and Helen laughed.
     (cause)   (effect)

Kristin and Douglas wore warm clothing because it was cold outside.
           (effect)   (signal)   (cause)

There are a number of words, such as *so* and *as a result of* that usually are clues to a cause/effect or effect/cause relationship. You can decide whether you want to introduce these words as signal words. These can be confusing for primary-grade students because the words *so* and *as a result of* can either signal a cause or an effect based on how they are used in a sentence. Tell children that the best way to figure out what is a cause or an effect is to ask the *why* and *what happened* questions.

Examples:
Joe was afraid of the noise, so he ran home.
    (cause)   (effect)

Celia let Nora play with her toys, so Nora would be happy.
    (effect)   (cause)

Sample Practices

Here are some sample practices that you can use with your students.

1. Jerod came inside when it started to rain.

Question:
What is the cause and effect in this sentence?

Answer:

Jerod came inside when it started to rain.
  (effect)   (cause)

2. Rita threw her books on the floor because she was angry.

Question:

What is the cause and effect in this sentence?

Answer:

Rita threw her books on the floor because she was angry
  (effect)   (signal)   (cause)

3. Barry didn't like the movie, so he left.
        (cause)   (effect)

Modeling Strategy

Mrs. Perry says to her students "When I read I always ask myself why something happened or why something took place. Then I ask myself what caused it to happen. When I ask myself these questions, they help me under-stand what I am reading.

"These questions also help me when I am writing a story. When we write a story, we want it to make sense. When something happens, we have to have a reason or reasons for its happening. What happens in the story should have a cause or causes."

Mrs. Perry then says "Let's look at some sentences together." Here they are:

1. Because Jill didn't feel well, she stayed inside. (cause - effect)
2. Nadine laughs a lot when she sees something funny. (effect - cause)
3. When Lee fell, he hurt his leg. (cause - effect)

"First I ask myself 'Why did Jill stay inside?' The reason is because she didn't feel well. The word *because* signals a cause. However, I already know it's a cause because the words 'she didn't feel well' answer the question 'Why.' I then ask myself, 'What happened?' That should give me the effect or the result. The effect or result is that Jill stayed inside." Mrs. Perry then asks her students to do the same for the other two sentences.

When working with young children, it is a good idea to introduce cause and effect relationships by using concrete examples. Here is how one first grade teacher, Mrs. Hill, does this. The children are sitting in their seats. Mrs. Hill has previously placed a bag with something in it in the middle of the floor. Mrs. Hill purposely trips over the bag. She stops, looks at the children, and says "Did you see what just happened?" The children say "Yes, you tripped." "You're correct," says Mrs. Hill. "I tripped. Why did I trip?" The children reply "Because there was a bag on the floor. You didn't see the bag." "Good," says Mrs. Hill. "Today we will be working with cause and effect. The cause tells us why something happened and the effect tells us what happened. Now, listen to this sentence—'Mrs. Hill tripped because there was a bag on the floor.' Let's see if someone can tell me what happened or the effect." "Good, Sharon, 'Mrs. Hill tripped' is correct. Now, who can tell me the cause or why it happened?" "Good, Seth, yes, the answer is 'because there was a bag on the floor.'

"Did you notice that the word *because* helps us figure out the cause, which is why something happens?" Mrs. Hill then asks her students to act out some cause and effect relationships that she gives them.

Mrs. Hill asks who would like to act out falling down and crying. After a child play acts falling down and crying, Mrs. Hill asks the children to tell what happened and why it happened—or the cause. Next she asks the children to construct a sentence telling what happened. Here are some of the sentences the children made up.

Amy cried when she fell.
Because Amy fell, she cried.
Amy cried because she fell.

Mrs. Hill goes over the sentences with the children and has the children tell what happened and why. She asks the children to notice how the word *because* helped them figure out the cause or why something happened. Also, even though the sentences are written differently, the cause and effect are the same. (Amy fell - cause); (Amy cried - effect)

Learning Objective

To figure out cause and effect relationships within the story.

Directions for Student Practices

Use the student practices on pages 52-56 to help your students acquire, reinforce, and review cause and effect. Pick and choose the practices based on the needs and developmental levels of your students. Answers for the student practice pages are on page 301.

When practicing finding cause and effect within a story, have the children read the story and then answer the questions. For those who have difficulty reading, read the story aloud to the children and orally ask them the questions.

Extensions

Role-Playing

Invite children to choose a cause-and-effect scene from a favorite story or make up their own scene with a cause and effect. Divide the class into small groups and encourage each group to act out their cause-and-effect scene for the class. Challenge the children watching the scenes to discover what is the cause and then what is the effect in each scene.

Cartoons

Invite children to choose a cause-and-effect situation from a favorite story or make up their own situation with a cause and effect. Then encourage children to draw cartoons of the situations. Ask each child to share his or her cause-and-effect cartoon with the class.

Write or Tell a Story

Ask students to write sentences on strips of paper that have a cause and effect. Place the paper strips in a large can. Once you have a variety of cause-and-effect sentences in the can, invite students to pull out a sentence (not their own) and use the sentences to write or tell their own stories.

Assessment Tool Progress Report

Progress

Improvement

Comments

Comprehension Strategies for an Integrated Language Arts Classroom © 1994 Fearon Teacher Aids

Name _____

Practice 1

Directions: Read the make-believe story about Zip and Zap, an imaginary cat and rat who live on the moon. Read the sentences that follow the story. State which part of the sentence is a cause and which is an effect. (Remember, why something happens is the *cause* and what happens is the *effect*.)

Today is a special day on the moon because it is Children's Day. Zip and Zap love this day because there are lots of parties. The parties are fun because the children play lots of games. Funny clowns do lots of tricks that make the children laugh. The children eat all the things they like and have fun all day long.

1. Today is a special day on the moon because it is Children's Day.

   _____

2. Zip and Zap love this day because there are lots of parties.

   _____

3. The parties are fun because the children play lots of games.

   _____

4. Funny clowns do lots of tricks that make the children laugh.

   _____

Comprehension Strategies for an Integrated Language Arts Classroom © 1994 Fearon Teacher Aids

Name _____

Practice 2

Directions: Read the make-believe story about Zip and Zap, an imaginary cat and rat who live on the moon. Read the sentences that follow the story. State which part of the sentence is a cause and which is an effect. (Remember, why something happens is the *cause* and what happens is the *effect*.)

Zip and Zap ate too much, so they got stomachaches. The next day, they both had to stay home because they did not feel well. They did not want to eat anything. They did not want to look at food because it made them sick. Zip and Zap went to see the doctor because their stomachs hurt so much. The doctor gave them medicine to make them feel better. Zip and Zap said that they would not eat so much ever again.

1. Zip and Zap ate too much, so they got stomachaches.

_____

2. The next day, they both had to stay home because they did not feel well.

_____

3. They did not want to look at food because it made them sick.

_____

4. Zip and Zap went to see the doctor because their stomachs hurt so much.

_____

Name _____

Practice 3

Directions: Read the short story. Read the sentences that follow the story. State which part of the sentence is a cause and which is an effect. (Remember, why something happens is the *cause* and what happens is the *effect*.)

Naomi and Phil didn't play outside for two days because their dads said it was too cold. Naomi and Phil, however, wanted to go outside and play. Naomi wanted to go see Phil. "No," said Naomi's dad, "It's too cold outside." "But, I don't have anything to do," said Naomi. "Phil has lots of games, so I want to visit him." It was no fun when it was too cold to play outside.

1. Naomi and Phil didn't play outside for two days because their dads said it was too cold._____

   _____

2. Phil has lots of games, so I want to visit him. _____

   _____

3. It was no fun when it was too cold to play outside. _____

   _____

Practice 4

Directions: Read the short story. Read the sentences that follow the story. State which part of the sentence is a cause and which is an effect. (Remember, why something happens is the *cause* and what happens is the *effect*.)

Karesha was bored because she didn't have anything to do. She tried to think of something to do. She thought and thought and thought. Then she asked her mother what she could do because she couldn't think of anything. "Why don't you read a book?" said Karesha's mother. "Your brother knows you love to read, so he brought you lots of new books from the library. Let's look at a few of the books together. I like this one because it is so funny," said her mother.

1. Karesha was bored because she didn't have anything to do. _____

_____

2. Then she asked her mother what she could do because she couldn't think of anything. _____

_____

3. Your brother knows you love to read, so he brought you lots of new books from the library. _____

_____

4. I like this one because it is so funny. _____

_____

Practice 5

Directions: Read the short story. Read the sentences that follow the story. State which part of the sentence is a cause and which is an effect. (Remember, why something happens is the *cause* and what happens is the *effect*.)

Burt went on vacation with his family to Mexico. Linda went with her family to Seattle because she wanted to visit her cousins. After their vacations, both Burt and Linda went back to school. Burt was very happy to see Linda. Linda was also happy to see Burt. "I like school because there are lots of things to do," said Burt. "Because I like to learn about things, I like school, too," said Linda. The children were all happy when Burt and Linda came back to school. Burt and Linda are a lot of fun, so the other children missed them.

1. Linda went with her family to Seattle because she wanted to visit her cousins.

   _____

2. I like school because there are lots of things to do. _____

   _____

3. Because I like to learn about things, I like school, too. _____

   _____

4. The children were all happy when Burt and Linda came back to school. _____

   _____

5. Burt and Linda are a lot of fun, so the other children missed them. _____

   _____

Strategy 4:
Finding the Main Idea of a Paragraph

Explanation

The main idea of a paragraph is what the paragraph is about. Without a main idea, a paragraph would just be a confusion of sentences. All the sentences in a paragraph should come together to develop the main idea.

Finding the main idea of a paragraph is a very important skill. It is also one in which children need a great amount of practice. It is not easy to find the main idea of a paragraph. Even if the main idea is directly stated, children still need to be able to figure out that it is, indeed, the main idea—there is no red flag identifying it.

Another problem with finding the main idea is that often children are asked to find the main idea of a paragraph that is not cohesive. In other words, the paragraph is not well written and may actually have more than one main idea. A paragraph must have only one main idea.

Special Note
Even though the procedures for finding the main idea of a paragraph and the central idea of a group of paragraphs are similar, finding the main idea and central idea are being presented separately. This helps to highlight the differences between finding the main idea of a paragraph and finding the central idea of a group of paragraphs. (See Strategy 5 on page 67.)

Teaching Strategies in Action

To find the main idea of a paragraph, students must determine what common element the sentences in the paragraph share. Although there is no foolproof method for finding the main idea, there is a widely used procedure that has proven to be very helpful.

Explain to your students that a paragraph is always written about someone or something. The someone or something is the topic of the paragraph. The writer is interested in telling his or her readers something about the topic of the paragraph. To find the main idea, your students must determine what the topic of the paragraph is and what the author is trying to say about the topic that is special or unique. Once students have found these two things, they should have the main idea.

> *Example:*
> Bonnie looked out the window and saw that it was a beautiful, sunny day. Bonnie put on her jacket and went outside. She decided to walk around the block and see what she could see. On her walk, she saw a bluebird, a squirrel, and a bright yellow flower. Bonnie was happy that she went on her walk.

The who or what of the paragraph is "Bonnie." The special or unique thing about Bonnie is that she took a walk and saw many things as she walked around the block. Therefore, the main idea of the paragraph is "Bonnie saw many things on her walk."

Sample Practices

Here are some sample practices that you can use with your students.

1. Have your students read the following one-paragraph story. Then have students chose the sentence that best states the main idea of the paragraph.

    Tom and Jim are upset. For the first time, they will not be in the same class. Tom and Jim are best friends. They have been in the same class since kindergarten. They like being together and doing their homework together. They also like being on the same class team. Now things will change.

    a. Tom and Jim are upset.
    b. Tom and Jim are best friends.
    c. Tom and Jim are upset because they will not be in the same class.
    d. Tom and Jim do everything together.
    e. Tom and Jim like doing things together.

    Answer: c. Tom and Jim are upset because they will not be in the same class. (Help children understand why this is the correct answer. Go over the other answers and explain why they are not correct. The other choices are all too specific—they are just details. Go over the correct answer and show how all the sentences in the paragraph develop the main idea.)

2. Present the following paragraph to your students:

    Sharon was sad. She felt like crying. She still couldn't believe it. Her best friend, Maria, had moved away. Her best friend had left her. What could she do?

    Ask your students what the topic of the paragraph is or about whom or what the paragraph is written.

    Answer: Sharon.

    Then ask your students what the writer is saying that is special about Sharon.

    Answer: Sharon is sad because her best friend moved away.

    Explain to your students that finding the main idea of the paragraph is finding who or what the paragraph is about and what is special about that who or what. Tell them that all the sentences should help develop the main idea. Go over each sentence with the children.

Modeling Strategy

Here is how Ms. Juarez models the technique for finding the main idea for the following paragraph.

Paul Jones wasn't a liar; he just exaggerated a lot. Paul exaggerated so much that people always expected him to exaggerate. Paul never disappointed them. Here are some examples of Paul's exaggerations. If Paul ate three pancakes, he'd say "I ate fifty pancakes." If he walked a mile, he'd say "I walked a hundred miles today."

After reading the paragraph, Ms. Juarez says "First I ask myself what is the topic of the paragraph? Asking the question who or what can help me get the topic, so I'll try that. Here are some of my choices." Ms. Juarez writes the following choices on the board while pointing out how she found these choices.

a. Lying
b. Paul's lying
c. Paul's exaggeration
d. Exaggeration

Ms. Juarez continues. "After looking at my choices, I choose c.—'Paul's exaggeration.' I choose it because it best answers what the paragraph is about, but I know that this is not the main idea; it is only part of it. I have to go on and ask myself some other things. Now, I have to decide what the writer is saying about Paul's exaggeration that is special and helps pull all the details together. Here are my choices." Ms. Juarez writes the choices on the board.

a. It is bad.
b. It is not a problem.
c. It is a problem.
d. It applies to everything he does.
e. It should not be allowed.

"I choose d.—'It applies to everything he does.' The topic is Paul's exaggeration, and what is special about it is that it applies to everything he does. Therefore, the main idea is 'Paul's exaggeration applies to everything he does.'"

After Ms. Juarez models this example, she uses other appropriate paragraphs to continue the modeling process with her students. She also asks her students to help her make the choices for finding the main idea of the paragraphs, continuing to say aloud the thinking process involved.

Learning Objective

To determine the main idea of a one-paragraph story and also supply a title for the story.

Directions for Student Practices

Use the student practices on pages 62-66 to help your students acquire, reinforce, and review finding the main idea of a paragraph. Pick and choose the practices based on the needs and developmental levels of your students. Answers for the student practice pages are on page 302.

When practicing finding the main idea within a story, have the children read the story and then answer the questions. For those who have difficulty reading, read the story aloud to the children and orally ask them the questions.

Special Note

In the directions section of the main idea practices, students are asked to find the main idea of a short one-paragraph story rather than of a paragraph. Usually a story has more than one paragraph. However, in working with young children, the use of the term *story* seems more appropriate.

Extensions

Idea Art

After reading a favorite story with the class, give each child a piece of paper. Read an appropriate paragraph or paragraphs from the story and invite the children to draw pictures showing the main idea of the paragraph. Encourage children to share their drawings with the rest of the class.

What's in a Name?

Invite students to choose paragraphs from a favorite story. Have the students read the paragraphs carefully or read them aloud together. Then encourage students to create titles for the chosen paragraphs.

Pantomime

Help children choose appropriate paragraphs from a favorite story. Or, have the children write short paragraphs. Divide the class into small groups and invite each group to pantomime the main idea of the chosen paragraph. Use different paragraphs for each group and invite the other children to guess what each group is pantomiming.

Character to Character

If students are reading a story having several characters, invite children to role-play each character. Have one of the characters tell another story character what the main idea of that particular paragraph is.

Student's Name _____

Assessment Tool Progress Report

Progress

Improvement

Comments

Name _____

Practice 1

Directions: Read the make-believe story about Zip and Zap, an imaginary cat and rat who live on the moon. Read the sentences that follow the story. Choose the sentence that best states the main idea of the story. Then write a title for the story that tells what the story is about.

Today is Zip and Zap's birthday. They were both born on the same day and every year they celebrate their birthdays together. They always have a party. They invite all the other boy and girl cats and rats. They eat cake and ice cream and have lots of fun. They play fun games and get lots of presents. Zip and Zap love their birthday parties.

1. Zip and Zap's birthday.

2. Zip and Zap like to have fun.

3. Zip and Zap always have a birthday party.

4. Zip and Zap's birthdays are fun.

5. Zip and Zap play games at their birthday party.

Title: _____

_____

_____

Comprehension Strategies for an Integrated Language Arts Classroom © 1994 Fearon Teacher Aids

Practice 2

Directions: Read the make-believe story about Zip and Zap, an imaginary cat and rat who live on the moon. Read the sentences that follow the story. Choose the sentence that best states the main idea of the story. Then write a title for the story that tells what the story is about.

Zip and Zap are not feeling very happy. They have just had their first fight. Zip and Zap have never had a fight before. Zip thought about the fight. Zap thought about the fight. They both felt sad.

1. Zip and Zap are sad.

2. Zip and Zap never had a fight before.

3. Zip and Zap's first fight makes them feel sad.

4. Zip and Zap's fight.

5. Zip and Zap fight with each other.

Title: _____

_____

_____

Name _____

Practice 3

Directions: Read the make-believe story about Zip and Zap, an imaginary cat and rat who live on the moon. Read the sentences that follow the story. Choose the sentence that best states the main idea of the story. Then write a title for the story that tells what the story is about.

Zip and Zap spend a lot of time in their house. They have to because it is very hot when the sun is out. It gets very cold when the sun is not out. On the moon, daylight lasts for 14 Earth days. Darkness or nighttime lasts for 14 Earth days, too.

1. It's cold on the moon.

2. Zip and Zap stay in their house a lot.

3. The moon's weather.

4. Zip and Zap's house.

5. The moon's weather forces Zip and Zap to stay in their house.

Title: _____

_____

_____

Practice 4

Directions: Read the short story. Write the main idea of the story. Then write a title for the story that tells what the story is about.

One beautiful, sunny day, a new family moved into a house in Beth's neighborhood. Everyone in the neighborhood was excited. For weeks and weeks, everyone had been talking about the new family's move to the neighborhood. The new family moved into a large house right next to Beth's house. The children in the new family, Jack and Melanie, would be able to play with Beth and her friends. They would also go to Beth's school. Soon the new family would be part of the neighborhood.

Main idea:_____

_____

_____

_____

Title:_____

_____

_____

Practice 5

Directions: Read the short story. Write the main idea of the story. Then write a title for the story that tells what the story is about.

Fiona got an invitation to a birthday party. She didn't feel like going to the party. Her mom asked her why she didn't want to go. "Because I won't know very many people there," she answered. Fiona's mom said "The more parties you miss, the more people you won't get to know." Fiona sat and thought about this. She thought about the blond-haired girl who seemed nice. She might be at the party and maybe they could be friends. Fiona thought about the funny boy with the purple tennis shoes. He's probably nice, too, she thought. "Maybe I'll go to the party after all," Fiona said.

Main idea:_____

_____

_____

_____

Title:_____

_____

_____

Comprehension Strategies for an Integrated Language Arts Classroom © 1994 Fearon Teacher Aids

Strategy 5:
Finding the Central Idea of a Story

Explanation

We generally use the term *central idea* when we refer to a group of paragraphs or a story. The technique for finding the central idea is similar to finding the main idea. The central idea is the central thought of the story. All the paragraphs of the story should develop the central idea.

In the primary grades, the term *main idea* is used more often than central idea. In this book, the two are being presented separately to show that there are differences between the two.

Teaching Strategies in Action

To find the central idea of a story, students must find the common element the paragraphs in the story share. Usually the first paragraph is very helpful because it often contains or anticipates the central idea.

As already stated, the procedure for finding the central idea is similar to that for finding the main idea. Help your students recognize that a story, like a paragraph, is written about someone or something. The "someone" or "something" is the topic of the story. The writer is interested in telling his or her readers something about the topic of the story. To find the central idea of the story, your students must determine what the topic of the story is and what the author is trying to say about the topic that is special or unique. Once they have found these two things, they should have the central idea.

> *Example*:
> Jerry wasn't happy about playing on the baseball team. His mom had signed him up. Even though he didn't really want to play, he thought he had to play anyway.
>
> It was the first day of practice and Jerry was late for the game. He forgot his baseball shoes, too. He even couldn't remember which field they were playing on. As Jerry was getting to the ball park, his mom pulled up in the car.
>
> "Jerry, wait!" she cried. "I just found out that your piano lesson has been rescheduled to Thursdays. That's today. I'm so sorry, Jerry. I guess you won't be able to play baseball on Thursdays."
>
> "I guess not," said Jerry, with a secret smile on his face.

In this short story, the topic of the story—the who or what—is Jerry. What is special about Jerry is that he is happy that he doesn't have to be on the baseball team. The central idea then is "Jerry is happy that he doesn't have to be on the baseball team." Students can find the central idea in the first paragraph.

Sample Practices

Here are some sample practices that you can use with your students.

1. Have your students read the following short story. Then have students chose the sentence that best states the central idea of the story.

   Jesse wanted some very special seeds. She wanted purple petunia seeds. Jesse wanted to plant the seeds in her garden.

   Jesse looked in three different stores to find the seeds. Finally, she found some purple petunia seeds at the fourth store. She took the seeds home and planted them in her garden. That spring, Jesse had beautiful purple petunias covering her garden.

   a. Purple petunia seeds.
   b. Jesse wanted purple petunia seeds to plant in her garden.
   c. Jesse went to four different stores that day.
   d. Purple petunias covered Jesse's garden.

Answer: b. Jesse wanted purple petunia seeds to plant in her garden.
(Help children understand why this is the correct answer. Go over the other answers and explain why they are not correct. The other choices are all too specific—they are just details. Go over the correct answer and show how the central idea can often be found in the first paragraph.)

2. Present the following story to your students:

   Tonya had fourteen teddy bears. She took very good care of the bears. Tonya always knew where they were. She would dress the bears and play with them and sit them all around the table for tea. Tonya would not let anyone else play with her bears. She wouldn't even let her little sister, Sarah, play with them—unless, of course, Sarah was invited to tea, too.

   One day, Tonya came home and found that her favorite bear, Sir Honeypot, was missing from his place on the bed. Tonya looked everywhere for Sir Honeypot—under the table, in the closet, even in the kitchen under the sink! Sir Honeypot was nowhere to be found.

   As Tonya walked past Sarah's room on her way to look in the bathroom, she peered in. There was Sarah, sitting on her bed, having a very involved discussion with Sir Honeypot. Tonya was angry at first. But then she decided that she would let Sarah and Sir Honeypot finish their "conversation."

   Ask your students what the topic of the story is or about whom or what the story is written.

Answer: Tonya.

   Then ask your students what the writer is saying that is special about Tonya.

Answer: Tonya looks all over for her favorite bear, Sir Honeypot, and finally finds him with her little sister, Sarah.

Explain to your students that finding the central idea of the story is finding who or what the story is about and what is special about the subject. Tell them that all the paragraphs should develop the central idea.

Modeling Strategy

Here is how Ms. Davis models this technique for the following short story.

Jeff had always wanted to be a basketball player. His goal was to make the school basketball team. His whole life was directed to making his dream come true. All he thought about was basketball. Everything he did was related to basketball. It was the most important thing in his life.

Jeff practiced for hours every day. He exercised, ate well, and slept at least eight hours a day. He only read books that had to do with basketball. He read the life stories of famous basketball players. Jeff could tell you almost anything you wanted to know about well-known basketball players.

After reading the story, Ms. Davis says "I begin by asking myself what is the topic of the story. In other words, who or what is this story about. It seems to me that the story is about Jeff's goal to be on the school basketball team. Both paragraphs talk about Jeff's goal to be on the basketball team. So the topic is 'Jeff's goal to be on the basketball team.'

"Now, I need to figure out what is special about Jeff's goal to be on the basketball team. It seems that for Jeff, being on the team is the most important thing in his life. Therefore, the central idea is 'Jeff's goal to be on the basketball team is the most important thing in Jeff's life.'

"I can check my central idea by rereading the first paragraph because, many times, a writer will state the central idea in the first paragraph. I also can check to see if all the paragraphs come together to develop the central idea."

Learning Objective

To state the central idea of a story and supply a title for the story.

Directions for Student Practices

Use the student practices on pages 72-76 to help your students acquire, reinforce, and review finding the central idea of a story. Pick and choose the practices based on the needs and developmental levels of your students. Answers for the student practice pages are on page 302.

When practicing finding the central idea of a story, have the children read the story and then answer the questions. For those who have difficulty reading, read the story aloud to the children and orally ask them the questions.

Extensions

Three-Panel Display

Invite children to make a three-panel cardboard display to illustration the central idea of a favorite story. Give each child a large piece of cardboard, approximately 1 1/2 feet long. Help children fold the boards in two spots, making three 8-inch panels. Then invite children to cover each of the panels with different-colored construction paper. Encourage children to use crayons, paint, or markers to decorate their panels. The first panel can show the main character or characters of the story. The second panel can be a picture of the topic—the who or what—of the story. The third panel can show what is special about the topic. Then invite each child to write or dictate the central idea of the story along the top or bottom of the three panels. Display in the classroom.

Story Posters

Invite each child to make a poster advertising a favorite story. Give each child a piece of posterboard or chart paper. Challenge the children to include the central idea of the story in each of their posters, either in drawings or in written words. Encourage the children to be creative.

Radio Advertisement

Have students write and record a pretend radio advertisement for a favorite story. Divide the class into small groups. Encourage the children in each group to work together to create an advertisement. Children should include the central idea of the stories in their ads. After the children have rehearsed their radio ads, invite each group to tape their ad on a tape recorder in another area of the classroom. Play the recordings for the rest of the class.

Write a Letter

Ask each student to write a letter to a friend or family member about a favorite book or story they are reading or have read. Encourage each student to include the central idea in their letter to help explain the story. Students can send the letters, if they wish.

Assessment Tool Progress Report

Progress

Improvement

Comments

Student's Name _____

Practice 1

Directions: Read the make-believe story about Zip and Zap, an imaginary cat and rat who live on the moon. Write the central idea of the story. Then write a title for the story that tells readers what the story is about.

One day, Zip said to Zap "Let's do something different."
"All right," said Zap, "but what shall we do?"
"I don't know," said Zip. "Let's think."

Zip and Zap sat and sat and sat. They thought and thought and thought.
Finally, Zap said "Let's play hide and seek."
"Oh, no," said Zip. "We always play that. I want to play something different."
"I know," said Zip. "Let's play pin-the-tail-on-the-donkey."
"Oh, no," said Zap. "We always play that. Let's play something different."
"It's hard to think of something different to do," said Zip. "I'm tired."
"So am I," said Zap, "so let's stop."

"You know," Zap said, "we did do something different today."
"That's true," said Zip. "We tried to think of something different to do, and it was hard work."

Central idea:_____

_____

_____

_____

Title:_____

_____

_____

Comprehension Strategies for an Integrated Language Arts Classroom © 1994 Fearon Teacher Aids

Student's Name _____

Practice 2

Directions: Read the make-believe story about Zip and Zap, an imaginary cat and rat who live on the moon. Write the central idea of the story. Then write a title for the story that tells readers what the story is about.

Zip and Zap were very excited. They were both born on the same day so they had the same birthday. They also had each received a moon bicycle as a birthday present. They couldn't wait to ride them.

After their birthday party, Zip and Zap put on their special moon clothing and their air masks. They went outside to ride their bicycles.

"Whee, look at me go," said Zip.
"Look at me! Look at me!" said Zap.
"Be careful," said Zip. "If you go over a bump, you will jump up, up, and away."
"I know," said Zap. "I won't hit any bumps."
Zip and Zap rode their bicycles for a long time. They didn't hit any bumps and had a lot of fun.

Central idea: _____

_____

_____

_____

Title: _____

_____

Practice 3

Directions: Read the short story. Write the central idea of the story. Then write a title for the story that tells what the story is about.

In a faraway country, there lived a very rich man who liked peace and quiet. This man lived in a large house. On one side of the man's house lived a carpenter. On the other side lived another carpenter. Day and night, you could always hear banging coming from both houses. The rich man knew he had to do something.

One day the rich man told both carpenters that he would give them lots of money if they would move. The carpenters were very happy to hear this. Each moved.

They went to the rich man to collect their money. They told him that they had moved. This made the rich man very happy. He gave them the money.

The next day the rich man heard banging from both sides. He rushed to see what it was. When he saw what was causing the banging, he was very angry. The two carpenters had moved. They had moved into one another's houses.

Central idea: _____

_____

_____

_____

Title: _____

_____

_____

Comprehension Strategies for an Integrated Language Arts Classroom © 1994 Fearon Teacher Aids

Practice 4

Directions: Read the short story. Write the central idea of the story. Then write a title for the story that tells readers what the story is about.

Once upon a time in Africa, there lived a cruel lion. This lion frightened all the animals in the jungle. No animal was safe from this lion. One day, the animals met and came up with a plan. The plan was not a very good one, but it was the best they could think of. Each day, one animal would go to the lion to be eaten by him. That way, the other animals would know that they were safe for a little while. The lion agreed to the plan, and that is how they lived for a time.

One day, it was the clever fox's turn to be eaten by the lion. Mr. Fox, however, had other plans. Mr. Fox went to the lion's cave an hour late. The lion was very angry. "Why are you so late? I am hungry," he said. Mr. Fox answered, "Oh, I am so sorry to be late, but another very, very big lion tried to catch me. I ran away from him so that you could eat me." When the lion heard about the other lion, he became more angry. "Another lion?" he asked. "I want to see him."

The fox led the lion through the jungle see the other lion. When they came to a well, the fox stopped. "The other lion is in there," said the fox, motioning toward the well. The lion looked into the well, and he did, indeed, see a lion. He got so angry that he jumped in the well to fight the lion. That was, of course, the end of the lion.

Central idea: _____

_____

_____

_____

Title: _____

_____

Practice 5

Directions: Read the story. Write the central idea of the story. Then write a title for the story that tells readers what the story is about.

There was once a princess who was very sad. She was so sad that she couldn't eat. Every day the princess grew thinner and thinner. "We must do something," said the queen to the king. "Yes, but what can we do?" asked the king. "We must speak to the wise men," said the queen.

The wise men were called to appear before the king and queen. The wise men told the king and queen that they had to find out why the princess was sad. Once the princess stopped being sad, she would eat. "That is wise," said both the king and queen together. With that, the wise men left. The king and queen went to the princess. "Why are you sad?" asked both the king and queen together. "I am sad because I have no one to play with," said the princess. "But everyone is your friend," said the queen. "I don't want grown-up friends. I want someone my own age," answered the princess. "If we find you someone to play with, will you stop being sad?" asked the king. "If you stop being sad, will you start eating again?" asked the queen. The princess answered "Yes" to both questions.

The king and queen called all their helpers. They told their helpers to find someone for the princess to play with. The helpers went into the village. They found a little girl the same age as the princess. They brought the little girl to the princess. The princess liked the little girl. The princess stopped being sad and started to eat. She stopped growing thinner and thinner.

Central idea: _____

_____

Title: _____

_____

Strategy 6:
Using Divergent Thinking

Explanation

Divergent thinking has to do with the many different ways of looking at things. The dictionary defines the word *divergent* as "differing from the standard." In other words, divergent thinkers are those who can look at things differently or in a more creative way. Good divergent thinkers are able to look beyond the obvious and come up with new or alternate solutions. Students should be encouraged to try to solve problems in many different ways and be intelligent risk-takers and make educated guesses.

Special Note

In this book, the divergent-thinking skill is being presented early in the text because students should be encouraged to engage in this type of thinking as early as possible.

Teaching Strategies in Action

Help your students recognize that divergent thinking requires that they go beyond the obvious and look for alternate ways to solve problems. Children need to know that they can look at things in many different ways. By "differing from the standard," they are not only being more creative, but this will help them solve problems and think things through in different ways.

Help children be more divergent thinkers with the following brainstorming activity.

> *Example*:
> Ask your students to state the many different uses of a brick. You should expect answers such as the following:
>
> A brick can be used to build a wall.
> A brick can be used as a bed warmer.
> A brick can be used to write with.
> A brick can be carved out and used as a bowl.
> A brick can be used as a paperweight.
> And so on…

If your students state only uses that include building, encourage the children to be more creative thinkers by going beyond the obvious uses of a brick. The most creative is to come up with some unique uses for bricks, such as some of the uses listed above. During brainstorming activities, encourage children to build on one another's ideas—anything goes. After the brainstorming session, take the time to talk about and evaluate the answers with the children.

Sample Practices

Here are some sample practices that you can use with your students.

1. Ask the children what they could do with one mitten. Some of the answers could be:

Wear the mitten on one hand and keep the other hand in your pocket.
Make a puppet out of the mitten.
Wear the mitten on your nose as a nose warmer.
Carry your pencils in the mitten.
Use the mitten as a cup warmer.
Unravel the mitten and knit a cap.

2. Read the following paragraph with your students. Invite students to answer the questions that follow.

Zach and Eric decided to go on a hike. They put on their hiking boots and set off on their hike. They hiked for a long time. Finally, they came to a huge mountain. In the side of the mountain was a dark cave. Zach looked inside. "Should we go in?" he asked Eric. Eric shook his head.

Questions:
1. Do you think Eric wanted to go into the cave? Why or why not?
2. What do you think was in the cave?
3. How do you think the story will end?

Modeling Strategy

Here is how Mr. Jackson models for his students how to answer divergent-thinking questions. He has the children read the following short selection and then the questions that follow the story.

Zip and Zap, a cat and rat who live on the moon, had just received new space suits. They wanted to try them out. They put on their suits and went outside. They floated and floated far away. Zip and Zap were so excited about their new suits that they didn't notice where they were going. "Zip, where are we?" asked Zap. "I don't know," replied Zip, "I was following you."

Questions:

1. What do you think Zip and Zap are going to do?
2. What do you think the suits look like? Draw a picture of one of the suits.
3. Write an ending to this story.

Mr. Jackson says "I just read the short story. I see from the story that Zip and Zap are so excited about their new suits that they are not thinking about anything else. While I was reading the story, I felt that this will probably get them into trouble. I wonder if their parents know they left. I wonder if anyone knows they are outside. This can be scary if it gets late.

"If I were Zip and Zap, I would try to find something familiar to help me figure out where I was. I picture the suits to be silver with large plastic domes for the heads. On the suits, there are lots of buttons. If I were Zip or Zap wearing one of the suits, I would press each button. Maybe one is a special remote control phone. In my ending, I would have Zip and Zap floating around until they are very tired. Then they would start pressing each button on their suits. One of the buttons would connect them to the control center in the large air-filled dome in which they live. Then Zip and Zap would hear voices on the other end. The cat and rat in charge would tell Zip and Zap which button to push so someone could guide them home."

Mr. Jackson then says to the children "Did you notice that I used the information from the story to write the ending? My ending has to make sense and relate to the story. Now, I want each of you to try to write an ending for the story."

Encourage children to share their new endings to the story. Ask each child who is sharing to go through what his or her thinking process was for the new ending.

Learning Objective

To go beyond the text to answer questions that require divergent thinking.

Directions for Student Practices

Use the student practices on pages 82-86 to help your students acquire, reinforce, and review divergent thinking. Pick and choose the practices based on the needs and developmental levels of your students. Answers for the student practice pages are on page 303.

When practicing divergent thinking, have the children read the story and then answer the questions. For those who have difficulty reading, read the story aloud to the children and orally ask them the questions.

Extensions

Write a New Ending or Sequel

Invite children to write new endings to a favorite story. Children can write or dictate the new endings and also illustrate the new endings to the stories. Or, challenge the children to write sequels to favorite stories, such as "'Married Life' by Cinderella" or "Whatever Happened to the Three Little Pigs?"

Add a Character

Divide the class into small groups. Invite each group to choose a situation from a favorite story. Encourage the children in each group to role-play the character or characters. Then challenge the children to add a new character to the story and see how the situation changes. Each group can role-play their new situations for the rest of the class.

New Settings

Have children rewrite or retell familiar stories with different settings, such as the desert, the Arctic, or the moon. Encourage children to also illustrate the different story settings.

What Would You Do?

Encourage students to keep journals of their thoughts and ideas as they are reading stories or books. Ask each student to include in his or her journal how they would solve a particular problem differently from the way a character in the story they are reading would. Invite students to share their ideas with the class, if they wish.

Advice Column

Ask students to role-play characters from a favorite story that have a particular problem. Students, in the role of the story characters, can write letters to an advice columnist asking for help in solving their problems. Students can switch letters and play the role of advice columnist by answering the letters and helping the particular characters solve their problems.

Student's Name _____

Assessment Tool Progress Report

Progress

Improvement

Comments

Comprehension Strategies for an Integrated Language Arts Classroom © 1994 Fearon Teacher Aids

Practice 1

Directions: Read the make-believe story about Zip and Zap, an imaginary cat and rat who live on the moon. Answer the questions following the story. Use the back of this sheet if you need more space to write.

One day, Zip and Zap were very excited. They had just heard some good news. Their Earth cousins were coming to visit them. They were coming on the space shuttle. Their Earth cousins had never been to the moon.
"What fun we will have," said Zap to Zip.
"I wonder what we should plan to do," said Zip.
"I wonder how long they will stay," said Zap.
"I wonder what we can give them as a present," said Zip.
"Let's make something that is special," said Zap.
"Good idea," said Zap. "Let's do it now."

1. What do you think Zip and Zap look like? Describe each one.

   _____

   _____

2. What do you think Zip and Zap's cousins look like? Describe them.

   _____

   _____

3. What kind of games do you think Zip and Zap will play with their cousins?

   _____

4. What do you think Zip and Zap will make for their cousins?

   _____

5. What presents do you think Zip and Zap's cousins may bring for Zip and Zap?

   _____

Comprehension Strategies for an Integrated Language Arts Classroom © 1994 Fearon Teacher Aids

Name _____

Practice 2

Directions: Read the make-believe story about Zip and Zap, an imaginary cat and rat who live on the moon. Answer the questions following the story. Use the back of this sheet if you need more space to write.

One day, Zip and Zap decided that they would try to see the "Big One." Zip and Zap had heard the older cats and rats talk about the "Big One." The older cats and rats said that no one had ever seen the "Big One." Well, Zip and Zap would try. Zip and Zap put on their outdoor clothes and went in search of the "Big One." They walked and walked. Then they walked some more. Finally, Zap said, "Let's stop, and take a nap." So Zip and Zap took a nap. When Zip and Zap took a nap, they dreamed about the "Big One." When Zip and Zap got up from their nap, they felt as if they had seen the "Big One."

1. What do you think the "Big One" is?

_____

_____

2. What do you think Zip and Zap's dreams about the "Big One" were?

_____

_____

3. What do you think the "Big One" looks like?

_____

_____

4. What do you think Zip and Zap will do next?

_____

_____

Name _____

Practice 3

Directions: Read the short story. Answer the questions following the story. Use the back of this sheet if you need more space to write.

Zeres lives in the forest. Zeres is a troll. Only animals in the forest can see trolls. Forest trolls usually come out at night and sleep during the day. Zeres is a special kind of troll. Zeres likes to play with children. The other trolls do not want Zeres to play with children. Children are not supposed to be able to see trolls. No human beings are supposed to be able to see trolls. Only the animals can see trolls.

This, however, does not stop Zeres. Every day when the other trolls are asleep, Zeres sneaks out. Zeres skips through the forest in search of children. When Zeres sees a child, Zeres claps, jumps up and down three times, and screams with glee.

The children like to play with Zeres. Zeres knows lots of fun things to do. Zeres also knows lots of things and takes the children to lots of places. Sometimes they go to the tops of mountains. Sometimes they go to deserts. Sometimes they go on a ship. Sometimes they fly to another land. The children love Zeres. Zeres is their best friend.

1. Do you think Zeres is a boy or girl? Why?

_____

_____

2. Describe Zeres. Tell what you think Zeres looks like.

_____

3. Make up an adventure that Zeres has with some children.

_____

_____

Comprehension Strategies for an Integrated Language Arts Classroom © 1994 Fearon Teacher Aids

Practice 4

Directions: Read the short story. Answer the questions following the story. Use the back of this sheet if you need more space to write.

A young man went to bed after eating a very big supper. While he was sleeping, he had a dream. He dreamed that he had gone for a walk. While walking, he stepped on a sharp nail. The dream was so real that the young man awakened. When he awakened, he rushed to put a bandage on his foot. He then went back to sleep. The next day, the young man went to town. His friend asked him why he was limping. The young man told him what had happened. His friend said "I have a good idea. The next time you go to sleep, wear your sandals." The young man listened to his friend. From then on, he wore his sandals to bed.

1. Make up another dream that the young man has.

   _____

   _____

2. Make up a silly dream that the young man has.

   _____

   _____

3. Make up another ending for the story.

   _____

   _____

4. Write about a dream that you have had.

   _____

   _____

Comprehension Strategies for an Integrated Language Arts Classroom © 1994 Fearon Teacher Aids

Name _____

Practice 5

Directions: Read the short story. Answer the questions following the story. Use the back of this sheet if you need more space to write.

Once upon a time there was a princess who believed everything she heard. This princess was a very nice person. Her only problem was that she believed everything anyone said to her. If you told her that the moon was made of cheese, she would believe you. She would also ask for a slice of it. If you told her that you could pick the stars and use them for lights, she would believe you. She would also ask for a star.

The king didn't know what to do. He loved his daughter, but he was upset about her problem. "What will happen when I am gone? She will believe anything. I must get her to say that something is not true," thought the king. The king had an idea. He called his advisers. He told them that he would give one wish to the person who would make the princess say "That is a lie."

People from all over tried to make the princess say "That is a lie." They made up silly stories, but the princess believed all of them. One day, a poor country boy came to talk to the princess. He said to her that he had seen her father, the king, in his town and that her father would not give any money or help to the people in his town. The princess looked at him. Her face turned red. She screamed "That is a lie. My father always helps people." "That's true," said the poor country boy. "Now, I have only one wish. I wish that you would marry me." The princess thought that was a nice idea. The king did, too. So the princess and the poor country boy were married and lived happily together.

1. Make up a silly story that the princess believes. _____

_____

_____

2. Make up another ending for the story. _____

_____

Comprehension Strategies for an Integrated Language Arts Classroom © 1994 Fearon Teacher Aids

Strategy 7:
Following Directions

Explanation

Following directions is a skill children will use throughout their lives. By helping children learn to follow directions carefully, you will also be helping them do better on tests, answer questions more easily, and become more able to supply information. Here are some things that you, the teacher, can do to help your students learn good techniques in following directions.

1. Give your students practice in following directions.
2. Encourage students to ask questions about any direction that they are not sure of or that seems confusing to them.
3. Help your students to understand how important the skill of following directions is.
4. Help your students to understand that the ability to follow directions requires concentration.
5. Explain to students that they should try to avoid reading things into directions that are not there.
6. Impress upon your students the importance of reading directions very carefully.

Teaching Strategies in Action

Help your students recognize the importance of being able to follow directions. Challenge students to give you examples of when people need to follow directions. For example, people most often follow directions when cooking, baking, taking medicine, driving, traveling, repairing, building, taking examinations, doing assignments, or filling out applications. There are hundreds of common activities that require the ability to follow directions. Help your students realize that scarcely a day goes by without the need to follow directions. After stressing the importance of directions, involve your students in following directions that you give orally.

Examples:

1. Say to the students "Write the number three on the board and clap your hands twice."

2. You can have the children try following directions with any number of simple directions. After you have done a few of these orally, put the following geometric figures and sentence on the board.

Put a circle around the second circle. Put an "X" in the first circle.

Read the directions with the children. Then ask for a volunteer to come to the board to carry out the directions. You could try a few of these with the children. To stress concentration, have them read the instructions once only and then carry them out.

Sample Practices

Here are some sample practices that you can use with your students.

1. List the following directions on the chalkboard or read the directions to the children.

   a. Place your hands on your hips with your feet together.
   b. Put your right foot out, heel to the floor.
   c. Bring your right foot back to original position.
   d. Put your left foot out, heel to the floor.
   e. Bring your left foot back to original position.
   f. Turn once around and clap your hands.

   Encourage the children to follow the directions once more. Explain that if they follow the directions correctly, they will be doing a little jig!

2. Give each student a sheet of paper. Write the following directions on the chalkboard or give the directions orally.

   a. Write the word *hello*.
   b. Change the "e" to an "a."
   c. Change the second "l" to an "a."
   d. Move the "h" so it directly follows the second "a."
   e. Place the second "a" where the "o" is and move the "o" to where the second "a" is.

   Explain to the children that if they followed directions carefully, they should have the word *aloha*, which means *hello* in Hawaiian.

Modeling Strategy

Mrs. Green feels it would help the children if she were to verbalize everything she thinks and does when she is doing a following-directions activity. She presents the children with the following on a sheet of paper:

A E G H 4 7 9 cat book down

Directions: If there is a fifth letter of the alphabet, put a circle around it. If the letter *G* comes directly after the letter *A* and before the letter *H*, put a circle around it. If there is a word the opposite of *up*, put a line under it. If there is a number that equals three less than 12, put a line under it. If there is a word that rhymes with *house*, put a circle around the word.

Mrs. Green also puts the same material on the chalkboard. She then says to the children "I need to read the directions carefully, so I'll do that first. I will make sure that I read every single word. After I read all the directions, I'll do each one carefully. All the directions begin with the word *if*. I better be careful because I may not have to do anything. The first direction says that if there is a fifth letter of the alphabet, put a circle around it. I know my alphabet. The fifth letter is *E*. There is an *E*, so I will put a circle around it." Mrs. Green draws a circle around the *E* on the board and invites the students to do the same on their papers.

Mrs. Green continues. "The second direction is a little more involved. I better be careful. I'll do it in parts. The first part says that if the letter *G* comes directly after the letter *A*... wait a moment. On the sheet of paper and on the board, the letter *G* comes directly after *E*. The important word is *directly*. *G* does come after *A*, but it doesn't come *directly* after *A*. I don't have to go any further because it is not true. I don't have to do anything."

Mrs. Green stops at this point and asks her students to do the rest of the directions with her. She goes over each direction with the children and shows them on the chalkboard what it should look like. Here is what the finished exercise should look like:

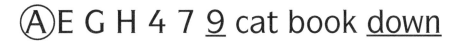

Learning Objective

To carry out written or oral directions.

Directions for Student Practices

Use the student practices on pages 92-101 to help your students acquire, reinforce, and review following directions. Pick and choose the practices based on the needs and developmental levels of your students. Answers for the student practice pages are on pages 303-304.

When practicing following directions, have the children read the directions and then answer the questions. For those who have difficulty reading, read the directions aloud to the children and orally ask them the questions.

Special Note

The student practices in this section do not have directions that ask the students to read the instructions once only. However, for older students, you might have them read the directions once only and then complete the practices.

Extensions

Simon Says

Lead the class in a game of "Simon Says." Gradually make the directions more and more complicated as the game goes on. You may also want to invite children to be the leaders of the game.

Let Me Tell You What to Do

Invite children to give directions. When doing the student practices, learning a game, or putting something together, invite one child to read the directions silently to himself or herself and then give directions to the others on what to do. Try to provide opportunities for all the students to read and explain directions.

Board Game

Invite students to make board games based on favorite stories or books. Divide the class into groups of 4 to 6. Using file folders as boards, show students how to make simple trails composed of small squares, each about one inch by one inch. Students can make the trails with "start" and "finish" squares. Encourage students to then decorate the boards with scenes from the books or stories. Have the students write directions for the games and then have each group share their game with the class.

Student's Name _____

Assessment Tool Progress Report

Progress

Improvement

Comments

Comprehension Strategies for an Integrated Language Arts Classroom © 1994 Fearon Teacher Aids

Name _____

Practice 1

Directions: Read each instruction carefully. Then carry the instructions out on the boxed material.

INSTRUCTIONS

1. Put the number *3* in the third square. Put the number *5* in the second circle.

2. Put the number *10* in the triangle. Put the number *2* in the first square.

3. Put a circle around the third circle. Put the number *1* in the third circle.

4. Put an "X" in the second square. Put an "X" on the triangle.

Comprehension Strategies for an Integrated Language Arts Classroom © 1994 Fearon Teacher Aids

Name _____

Practice 2

Directions: Read each instruction carefully. Then carry the instructions out on the boxed material.

INSTRUCTIONS

1. Put the number *9* in the third triangle. Put the number *4* in the second circle.

2. Put the letter *R* in the second square. Put a circle around the fourth triangle.

3. Put an "X" on the first, second, and fifth triangles. Put a circle around the first circle.

4. Put the third letter of the alphabet in the first circle. Put the next to the last letter of the alphabet in the third square and the third circle.

Name _____

Practice 3

Directions: Read each instruction carefully. Then carry the instructions out on the boxed material.

INSTRUCTIONS

1. Put the letter *D* in the third circle. Put the number *5* in the first triangle.

2. Put the number that equals 3 + 4 in the first circle. Put the number that equals 4 + 5 in the second square.

3. Put the number that equals 5 + 7 in the second triangle. Put the letter that comes before *F* in the second circle.

4. Put the letter that comes after *R* in the fourth circle. Put the three letters that come before *P* above the first square.

Comprehension Strategies for an Integrated Language Arts Classroom © 1994 Fearon Teacher Aids

Name _____

Practice 4

Directions: Read each instruction carefully. Then carry the instructions out.

1. Make three circles, two squares, and one triangle. Put a circle around the second circle.

2. Make a square, a triangle, and a circle, one after the other. Put an "X" on each.

3. Make two circles, one triangle, and four squares. Put the letter that comes before *G* in the first circle, the letter that comes after *L* in the triangle, and the letter that comes before *Q* in the first square.

4. Make four circles. Put the odd number after five in the first circle, the even number after eight in the last circle, and the letter before *D* in the third circle.

5. Write the odd numbers from one to seven. Write the even numbers from four to ten. Write the four letters of the alphabet that come before *S*.

6. Make six triangles and one square. Put a circle around each of the first four triangles. Put an "X" inside the square.

Practice 5

Directions: Read carefully the entire list of directions that follow before doing anything. You have three minutes to finish this activity.

1. Add 5 and 5.

2. Add 17 and 14.

3. Write the last three letters of the alphabet.

4. Write all the odd numbers in the numbers from 1 to 10.

5. Write all the even numbers in the numbers from 1 to 10.

6. Write your name at the top of the paper.

7. Write your address at the bottom of the paper.

8. Write the first five letters of the alphabet.

9. Make three squares.

10. Make three triangles.

11. Make a circle, a square, and a triangle.

12. Raise your right hand.

13. Lower your right hand.

14. Turn your paper upside down.

15. Call out "I am nearly finished."

16. Call out "I am the best direction follower."

17. Now that you have finished reading everything, do only numbers 6 and 7.

Name _____

Practice 6

Directions: Read each instruction carefully. Then carry the instructions out on the boxed material.

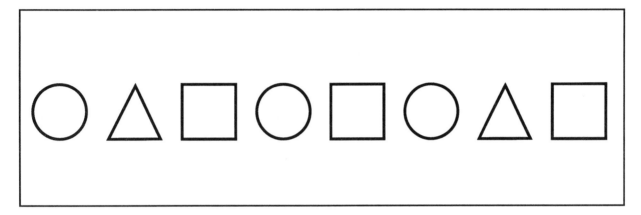

INSTRUCTIONS

1. If there are three circles and three triangles, put the first letter of the alphabet in the second triangle.

2. If there are the same number of squares as circles, put the letter that comes before *P* in the third circle.

3. If there are more circles than triangles, put the sum of 6 + 5 in the first square.

4. If there are three different figures one after the other, put a circle around all the circles.

Name _____

Practice 7

Directions: Read each instruction carefully. Then carry the instructions out on the boxed material.

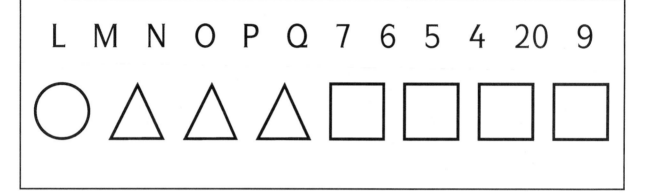

INSTRUCTIONS

1. If there are more letters than numbers, put an "X" in the first square.

2. If there are two numbers that added together equal another number in the boxed material, put a circle around the second triangle.

3. If there are more squares than triangles and the same number of letters as numbers, put the first letter in the boxed material after the third triangle.

4. If there are the same number of odd numbers as even numbers and if two numbers added together equal 11, put the number that comes before 6 in the boxed material in the third square.

Name _____

Practice 8

Directions: Read each instruction carefully. Then carry the instructions out on the boxed material.

1. cat L M N O P 7 6 5 4 man

2. boy in E F G out fat pan

3. ▢ ▢ △ ◯

4. ◯ ◯ ◯ ◯

5. △ △ ▢ ▢

INSTRUCTIONS

1. If there are two words that rhyme with *bat* and one word that rhymes with *pin*, put a circle around the two words that rhyme with *bat*.

2. If there are more circles than squares and if there are more squares than triangles, put an "X" on the word that is the opposite of *girl*.

3. If there are more letters than words and if there are fewer numbers than letters, put a circle around the middle letter in the second row.

4. If there are the same number of squares in row three as in row five and if there are the same number of even numbers as odd numbers, put an "X" above the triangle in the third row.

Name _____

Practice 9

Directions: Read each instruction once only. Then carry each instruction out on the circle.

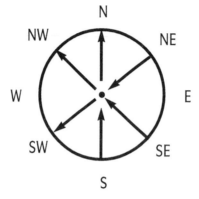

INSTRUCTIONS

1. If the arrows point in all the directions in the circle, put a circle around *NE*.

2. If the arrows point to *N*, *S*, and *NW*, put a circle around *S*.

3. If the arrows point to *N*, *SW*, and *NW*, put an "X" on *N*.

4. If there are more arrows pointing *NW* than *NE*, and if there are two arrows pointing *SW*, put a circle around *E*.

Practice 10

Directions: Read each instruction once only. Then carry each instruction out on the circles.

Circle A

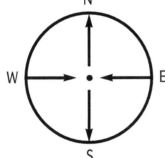

Circle B

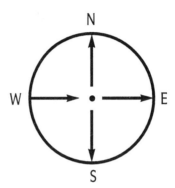

INSTRUCTIONS

1. If the arrows in Circle A are pointing in the same directions as the arrows in Circle B, put a circle around *E* in Circle A.

2. If the arrows in Circle A are pointing in four different directions, and if the arrows in Circle B are pointing in four different directions, put a circle around *W* in Circle B.

3. If the arrows in Circle B are pointing toward *E* and *N*, and the arrows in Circle A are pointing toward *E* and *N*, put a circle around *S* in Circle A.

4. If the arrows in Circle A are pointing toward *E* and *W*, and the arrows in Circle B are pointing toward *E* and *W*, put a circle around *N* in Circle B.

Strategy 8:
Categorizing

Explanation

The ability to divide items into categories is a very important thinking skill. As children advance through the grades, they should be able to differentiate and group items into more complex categories. Primary-grade children should be able to categorize a cat as distinct from a mouse or a rabbit. They should also be able to group the words *cat, dog,* and *cow* together as animals. As children develop their thinking skills, they should be able to proceed from more generalized classifications to more specialized classifications.

Teaching Strategies in Action

Help your students recognize that every time they put things into groups, such as pets, farm animals, wild animals, cities, states, countries, capitals, fruits, vegetables, colors, and so on, they are using the skill of categorizing. When they categorize things, they are classifying things. To be able to classify things, they must know what belongs together and what does not belong together. You can help your students to classify or categorize things into more general or more specific categories.

Example:
zucchini, carrot, peanut, orange, cashew, lettuce, apple

The category of *food* is more general than the categories of *fruits, vegetables,* or *nuts.*

Example:
dog, lion, horse, tiger, elephant, goat, cat, mouse, bird

The category of *animals* is more general than the categories of *pets, wild animals,* or *tame animals*. The category of *pets* is less general than the category of *animals*, but more general than the categories of *dogs* or *cats*.

Sample Practices

Here are some sample practices that you can use with your students.

1. Write the following list of animals on the chalkboard.

   lion, deer, dog, cat, tiger, parakeet, hamster, panther

   Then write the headings *pets* and *wild animals* on the chalkboard. Help the children categorize the animals previously listed into these two new categories.

pets	wild animals
dog	lion
cat	tiger
parakeet	deer
hamster	panther

2. List the following words on the chalkboard. Then ask students to put the words into two categories.

car, rowboat, spaceship, motorcycle, yacht, airplane, truck, bus, helicopter

Explain to students that these are all modes of transportation. They can be categorized as follows:

land transportation	water transportation	air transportation
car	rowboat	airplane
truck	yacht	helicopter
motorcycle		spaceship
bus		

Modeling Strategy

Here is how Mr. Mason helps the children learn about categorizing. He presents the children with the following group of words:

pear, celery, milk, apple, cheese, carrot, plum, butter, banana, spinach

Mr. Mason then says "I want to group these words into categories. First I look at each of them. They are all things we eat. They are all foods. The group *food* is a very big one. I would like to divide the *food* category into smaller groups. Let me look again at the words. I see fruits, vegetables, and dairy products. I think I can divide the words further into these three groups. Under *fruits*, I will put pear, apple, plum, and banana. Under *vegetables*, I will put celery, carrot, and spinach. Under *dairy products*, I will put milk, cheese, and butter." Mr. Mason then puts the following on the chalkboard:

vegetables	dairy products	fruits
celery	milk	pear
carrot	cheese	apple
spinach	butter	plum
		banana

Mr. Mason then asks the students to give examples of other foods that would fit into each group. As the children state the foods and their category, Mr. Mason puts these on the chalkboard under the correct heading.

Learning Objective

To classify items into categories in general and specific classifications.

Directions for Student Practices

Use the student practices on pages 106-125 to help your students acquire, reinforce, and review categorizing. Pick and choose the practices based on the needs and developmental levels of your students. Answers for the student practice pages are on pages 305-307.

When practicing categorizing, have the children read the directions and then answer the questions. For those who have difficulty reading, read the directions aloud to the children and orally ask them the questions.

Special Note

The student practices that are presented for your students are based on graduated levels of difficulty. The first few practices deal with pictorial representations of various items that should be familiar to your students.

Extensions

Categorizing Rocks

Provide the children with a box of assorted rocks. Invite children to think up ways they can categorize the rocks, such as by color, size, shine, shape, or texture.

Character Traits

Divide the class into groups. Invite the children in each group to choose characters from a number of favorite books or stories. Help children write the names of the characters on small strips of paper. Then challenge the children to arrange the character names in groups based on their common traits, such as clever, funny, silly, and so on.

Similar Settings

Write three or four story settings on cardboard signs and place the signs around the classroom. Then invite students to take books from the class library that they have read and categorize the books according to their settings.

Genre

Encourage students to choose a favorite story or book they are currently reading and tell what category the book belongs in—adventure, mystery, fiction, humor, nonfiction, fantasy, science fiction, and so on. Then invite students to form groups according to what category their book is in and share their books orally with one another.

Student's Name _____

Assessment Tool Progress Report

Progress

Improvement

Comments

Practice 1

Directions: Cut out the pictures and paste the pictures according to their groups—
vegetables, fruits, or *drinks*—on a blank sheet of paper.

milk

corn on the cob

water

pear

lemon

tomato

carrot

beet

cherries

soda pop

apple

potato

banana

Comprehension Strategies for an Integrated Language Arts Classroom © 1994 Fearon Teacher Aids

Name _____

Practice 2

Directions: Cut out the pictures and paste the pictures according to their groups—
pets, farm animals, or *wild animals*—on a blank sheet of paper.

elephant

ape

chicken

cat

parrot

cow

hippopotamus

lion

giraffe

dog

horse

tiger

Practice 3

Directions: Group the various items below under these headings on a blank sheet of paper: *furniture, things used for eating*, and *appliances*.

knife

bed

sofa

iron

dresser

fork

plate

toaster

spoon

oven

refrigerator

cup

Comprehension Strategies for an Integrated Language Arts Classroom © 1994 Fearon Teacher Aids

Name _____

Practice 4

Directions: Group the shapes in as many ways as you can on a blank sheet of paper. You can draw the shapes to make the various groups.

Practice 5

Directions: Group the cards in as many ways as you can on a blank sheet of paper.

Comprehension Strategies for an Integrated Language Arts Classroom © 1994 Fearon Teacher Aids

Name _____

Practice 6

Directions: First read the list of words. Then group the words in at least seven different ways.

hen	kitten	ape
drake	goose	tiger
sow	pig	goat
mare	dog	mule
colt	turkey	horse
gander	duck	puppy
elephant		

Name _____

Practice 7

Directions: First read the list of words. Then group the words in at least seven different ways.

chalk	chalkboard	library	jump rope
checkers	science books	desk	auditorium
basketball	pencil	classroom	pen
paper	principal	baseball	chess
student	history books	nurse	spelling books
teacher	monopoly		

Comprehension Strategies for an Integrated Language Arts Classroom © 1994 Fearon Teacher Aids

Name _____

Practice 8

Directions: First read the list of words. Then group the words in at least seven different ways.

scarf	watch	shoes	sweater	pants
socks	bracelet	coat	earrings	slip
cap	stockings	gloves	blouse	tights
shirt	vest	slippers	hat	mittens
dress	jeans	gown	skirt	boots

Name _____

Practice 9

Directions: Read the words in the word list. Choose a word from the word list that would belong in one of the groups listed below. All words from the word list are used as answers. The first is done for you.

Word List: coat, green, circle, milk, Terry, checkers, cat, ten

1. foods   ___milk___

2. colors   _____

3. clothing   _____

4. animals   _____

5. shapes   _____

6. numbers   _____

7. games   _____

8. names   _____

Comprehension Strategies for an Integrated Language Arts Classroom © 1994 Fearon Teacher Aids

Practice 10

Directions: Read the words in the word list. Choose a word from the word list that would belong in one of the groups listed below. All words from the word list are *not* used as answers. The first is done for you.

Word List: peas, carrots, yellow, white, purse, ring, gloves, plums, peaches, raisins, spinach, bread, checkers, football, candy, brown, gown, bathing suit

1. dried fruits   <u>raisins</u>

2. dark colors   _____

3. outdoor games   _____

4. indoor games   _____

5. cold weather clothing   _____

6. hot weather clothing   _____

7. leafy vegetables   _____

8. jewelry   _____

Name _____

Practice 11

Directions: Read the word list. Then choose a word from the word list that would belong to each group of words listed below and add it to the group. All words from the word list are used as answers.

Word List: crayon, wood, ant, goose, Frank, purple, Susan, spinach, circle, door

1. George, Max, Steve   _____

2. carrot, beet, bean   _____

3. blue, red, orange   _____

4. chimney, window, roof   _____

5. chalk, pen, pencil   _____

6. coal, oil   _____

7. wasp, fly   _____

8. Mary, Tara, Kathy   _____

9. triangle, oval, square   _____

10. duck, chicken, turkey   _____

Name _____

Practice 12

Directions: Read the word list. Then choose a word from the word list that would belong to each group of words listed below and add it to the group. All words from the word list are *not* used as answers.

Word List: doe, mustard, clothing, pants, eggs, chalkboard, lettuce, raisin, banana, dishwasher, food, six, twenty, candy, eight, seven, lady, princess, sixteen, nineteen, bread

1. apple, pear, plum _____

2. five, ten, fifteen _____

3. one, three, five _____

4. ten, twelve, fourteen _____

5. king, prince, queen _____

6. hen, ewe, mare _____

7. oven, stove, refrigerator _____

8. two, four, six _____

9. ketchup, relish, mayonnaise _____

10. desk, teacher, student _____

Practice 13

Directions: Read the word list. Then choose a word from the word list that would belong to each group of words listed below and add it to the group. All words from the word list are *not* used as answers. A word may be used only once.

Word List: pleasant, tired, thin, wide, large, pretty, leaf, cruel, school, reading, cat, subject, pet

1. big, great _____

2. good-looking, handsome _____

3. nice, friendly _____

4. mean, nasty _____

5. bark, branch _____

6. spelling, arithmetic _____

7. hamster, dog _____

Comprehension Strategies for an Integrated Language Arts Classroom © 1994 Fearon Teacher Aids

Name _____

Practice 14

Directions: Read each group of words. Try to figure out how they belong together. Then read the word list. Choose a word from the word list that best describes each group. All words from the word list are used as answers. The first one is done for you.

Word List: names, nuts, flowers, fowl, fruits, vegetables, meat, clothing, colors, shapes

1. celery, lettuce, peas, beans   <u>vegetables</u>

2. triangle, circle, square   _____

3. duck, chicken, turkey, goose   _____

4. almond, pecan, acorn   _____

5. mittens, hat, dress, coat   _____

6. gold, purple, red, blue   _____

7. Elena, Theo, Sally, Jack   _____

8. banana, apple, grape   _____

9. rose, mums, tulip   _____

10. pork, lamb, beef   _____

Practice 15

Directions: Read each group of words. Try to figure out how they belong together. Then read the word list. Choose a word or phrase from the word list that best describes each group. All words from the word list are *not* used as answers.

Word List: clothing, boys' names, girls' names, names, house things, kitchen things, eating things, bedroom things, food, sweets, tools, school things, writing things, fruit, dried fruit

1. Tasha, Maria, Jane _____

2. George, Paulo, Jerome _____

3. bed, pillow, blanket _____

4. spoon, fork, knife _____

5. prunes, raisins _____

6. crayon, pencil, magic marker _____

7. hammer, saw, pliers _____

8. cookies, candy, cake, apple, bread _____

Practice 16

Directions: First read the words in each group. Three of the words in each group belong together and one does not. Circle the word in each group that does not belong. The first is done for you.

1. winter, summer, (night) fall

2. December, July, January, February

3. carrot, pea, bean, lime

4. fairy tales, history books, science books, biographies

5. train, truck, car, airplane

6. motorcycle, bicycle, car, scooter

7. fifteen, twenty, twenty-five, twenty-eight

8. California, Ohio, United States, Florida

9. sow, doe, ewe, bull

10. whale, shark, salmon, tuna

Name _____

Practice 17

Directions: First read the words in each group. Three of the words in each group belong together and one does not. Circle the word in each group that does not belong. The first is done for you.

1. one, nine, (blue,) three

2. duck, goose, chicken, pig

3. basketball, baseball, ice hockey, football

4. violin, harp, cello, piano

5. two, five, three, one

6. eyes, hair, mouth, nose

7. gander, hen, rooster, drake

8. Europe, England, Spain, Mexico

9. raisin, plum, pear, apple

10. fin, hoof, gill, scale

Comprehension Strategies for an Integrated Language Arts Classroom © 1994 Fearon Teacher Aids

Practice 18

Directions: First read the words in each group. Three of the words in each group belong together and one does not. Circle the word in each group that does not belong. The first is done for you.

1. kitten, puppy, cub, (duck)

2. China, Asia, North America, Africa

3. east, west, north, right

4. dog, cat, ape, horse

5. drake, mare, rooster, ram

6. milk, cheese, meat, butter

7. student, pupil, learner, teacher

8. cupboard, bag, pantry, closet

9. ham, pork, bacon, beef

10. vest, coat, cape, hat

Name _____

Practice 19

Directions: First read the words in each group. Three of the words in each group belong together and one does not. Circle the word in each group that does not belong. The first is done for you.

1. purple, red, (seven) green

2. doe, duckling, puppy, kitten

3. mule, lion, tiger, ape

4. rose, carnation, tree, pansy

5. salt, pepper, sugar, cloves

6. sandal, slipper, shoe, sock

7. sty, stable, silo, coop

8. saw, pliers, knife, scissors

9. chair, bed, bunk, cot

10. beagle, fox, collie, terrier

Name _____

Practice 20

Directions: First read the words in each group. Three of the words in each group belong together and one does not. Circle the word in each group that does not belong. The first is done for you.

1. China, Germany, (Africa,) France

2. crow, canary, eagle, robin

3. large, long, huge, enormous

4. single, individual, silent, alone

5. rooster, mare, gander, drake

6. palace, castle, mansion, cabin

7. chirp, bark, bray, bell

8. pouch, bag, purse, drawer

9. scarf, necklace, ring, watch

10. frogs, snakes, turtles, lizards

Strategy 9:
Completing Word Relationships (Analogies)

Explanation

Analogies are the relationships between words and ideas. Certain words have relationships to one another, such as *night* and *day* (opposites) or *fruit* and *banana* (classification). Working with analogies requires high-level thinking skills. Students must have a good stock of vocabulary as well as the ability to see the relationships between the words or ideas.

Teaching Strategies in Action

Some primary-grade level children can begin to be exposed to simple analogies based on word relationships with which they are familiar. In order to be able to make the best use of analogies or to complete an analogy statement or proportion, the children must know the meanings of the words and the relationship of the pair of words.

> *Example:*
> Sad is to happy as good is to _____.

Many primary-grade level children know the meaning of the words *sad* and *happy* and that *sad* is the opposite of *happy*. Therefore, children would usually be able to complete the analogy statement or proportion with the correct word—*bad*.

There are many relationships that words may have to one another, such as similar meanings, opposite meanings, classification, going from particular to general, going from general to particular, degree of intensity, specialized labels, characteristics, cause-effect, effect-cause, function, whole-part, ratio, and many more. Explain to your students that they can gain clues to the word relationships from the pairs making up the analogies—that is, the words themselves express the relationship.

> *Example*:
> *pretty* is to *beautiful*—the relationship is degree of intensity (the state of being stronger, greater, or more than).
> *hot* is to *cold*—the relationship is one of opposites.
> *car* is to *vehicle*—the relationship is one of classification.

It would probably be a good idea for you to review the word lists of the presented analogy practices to determine whether your students are familiar with the vocabulary. You can encourage students to use dictionaries to look up any unfamiliar words.

The analogy practices (pages 132-146) can be done in small groups or with the entire class orally as well as individually. If children work individually on the analogy practices, you may want to go over the answers together so that interaction and discussion can further enhance children's vocabulary development.

Sample Practices

Here are some sample practices that you can use with your students.

1. Black is to white as night is to _____.

   Answer: day

   Explain to children that *black* is the opposite of *white*. So children need to find the opposite of *night*, which is *day*.

2. Dog is to puppy as cat is to _____.

   Answer: kitten

   A *puppy* is a baby *dog*, so students need to find what a baby *cat* is called, which is a *kitten*.

3. Hand is to mitten as head is to _____.

   Answer: hat

   A *hand* wears a *mitten* to stay warm. So students need to find what keeps a *head* warm, which is a *hat*.

Modeling Strategy

Here is how Ms. Gerber helps her students work with verbal analogies. Ms. Gerber writes the following sets of words on the chalkboard:

happy is to sad   bad is to good
big is to little   fat is to thin

She asks the children to read the sets of words to see how they go together. Ms. Gerber says she will do the same. Ms. Gerber then reads aloud the sets. She says "Let me see, *happy* is the opposite of *sad*. *Bad* is the opposite of *good*. *Big* is the opposite of *little* and *fat* is the opposite of *thin*. The words in the sets are all opposites." She then writes the following on the chalkboard:

Happy is to sad as bad is to good. Big is to little as fat is to thin.

Ms. Gerber asks the children to read the sets of words and tell her what they notice. Ms. Gerber says she will do the same.

She reads aloud the first set and says "In the first example, the first set has word opposites and the second set has word opposites. In the second example, the first set has word opposites and the second set also has word opposites. What I notice is that the first and second sets have the same kinds of pairs."

Ms. Gerber then presents the children with the following sets and tells them that they go together in some way.

big is to large   small is to little
finish is to end   start is to begin

Ms. Gerber says aloud her thoughts as she figures out that all these sets are words with the same meaning. She then puts on the chalkboard the following sets and asks the children what they can tell her about the sets.

Big is to large as small is to little.
Finish is to end as start is to begin.
Happy is to sad as bad is to good.
Big is to little as fat is to thin.

Ms. Gerber says "What I notice again is that the first and second sets of each sentence have the same kinds of pairs. Here are some more sets. Let's see if it's true for these also.

Fall is to season as March is to month.
Apple is to fruit as pea is to vegetable.

"Let me see, *fall* is a season. It is an example of a season. *March* is a month. It is an example of a month. Both sets in the pair are examples. *Apple* is an example of a fruit, and *pea* is an example of a vegetable. The first set has an example and the second set has an example. I see again that when two sets are put together, they have the same kinds of pairs." Ms. Gerber presents the children with the following and asks the children to try to figure out the word relationships.

Daughter is to child as aunt is to relative.

Ms. Gerber asks the children if they noticed that the first set has an example (daughter is to child). She mentions that a *daughter* is a kind of *child*. She then states that the second set also has an example (aunt is to relative). She tells the children that an *aunt* is a kind of *relative*. Ms. Gerber then asks her students to tell her what they learned. Many children raise their hands. Ms. Gerber calls on Seth. Seth says "When two sets are put together, they must have the same kinds of pairs." "Yes, good," says Ms. Gerber. She then gives the children some verbal analogy exercises to do on their own. Ms. Gerber tells the children she will go over these together with them. However, first she will do one for them, so they can see what she does to get the correct answer. Here is the example:

Autumn is to fall as wealthy is to _____. (poor or rich)

Ms. Gerber tells her students that in order to work with word sets, they must know the meanings of the words. If the students do not know the meanings of the words in the sets, they cannot figure out the relationship between the words. "I know," Ms. Gerber says, "that *autumn* is a season and *fall* is a season. I also know that autumn and fall are the same. They have the same meaning. Therefore, the words in my second set must also have the same meaning. Both sets must have the same kinds of pairs. Therefore, the answer must be *rich*. *Rich* is the same as *wealthy*. They share the same meaning." Now Ms. Gerber feels her students are ready to try the exercises

on their own. "Of course, I am here to help anyone who needs help,"
Ms. Gerber says before the students begin.

Special Notes

You may want to use the term *word relationships* with the students rather than *analogies*. You might want to introduce the term *analogy* to some of your older students.

In introducing some of the relationships that pairs of words can have to one another, try to use words that are in your students' listening vocabulary—that is, children have heard the words and know their meanings. The list of some possible relationships (page 126) is presented as an aid for you, the teacher.

You might want to help students recognize that there may be different ways to describe the relationship between a set of words.

> *Example:*
> hammer is to tool

This word relationship can be particular to general, classification, or example.

Learning Objective

To understand the relationships or analogies between words or ideas.

Directions for Student Practices

Use the student practices on pages 132-146 to help your students acquire, reinforce, and review completing word relationships or analogies. Pick and choose the practices based on the needs and developmental levels of your students. Answers for the student practice pages are on pages 308-309.

When practicing completing word relationships, or analogies, have the children read the directions and then answer the questions. For those who have difficulty reading, read the directions aloud to the children and orally ask them the questions.

Special Note

The practices that are presented for your students are based on graduated levels of difficulty. The first eight practices deal with pictorial representations of various items that should be familiar to your students. Special teacher instructions are provided for these eight exercises:

Practices 1 and 2

Present the picture sets to the children. Explain to children that the sets of pictures belong together in some way. Each set has a missing picture. Have each child look at the first pair of pictures in the set. Challenge children to figure out how the pictures belong together. Then have each child choose a picture from the large box that would *best* complete the second pair in the set. Encourage each child to draw a line from the picture in the large box to the appropriate empty space. All the pictures from the large box are used as answers. Do the example with the children.

Practices 3 and 4

The instructions for Practices 3 and 4 are the same as above. However, all the pictures in the large box are *not* used as answers. Do the example with the children.

Practices 5 and 6

Present the word and picture sets to the children. Explain to the children that the sets of words and pictures belong together in some way. Each set has a missing picture. Have each child look at the first word and picture pair of the example. Challenge children to try to figure out how the words and pictures belong together. Then have each child choose a picture from the large box that would *best* complete the second pair in the set. Encourage each child to draw a line from the picture in the large box to the appropriate empty space. For Practice 6, all pictures in the large box are *not* used as answers.

Practices 7 and 8

Present the picture and word sets to the children. Explain to the children that the sets of pictures and words belong together in some way. Each set has a missing word. Have each child look at the first picture and word pair of the example. Challenge children to figure out how they belong together. Then have each child choose a word from the large box that would best complete the second pair in the set. Encourage each child to write the word in the blank. For Practice 8, all words are *not* used as answers.

Extensions

Analogies in Literature Mural

Invite students to choose a favorite book or story. Help the students find analogies within the story, such as nice to mean characters, characters to settings, or characters to problems. Then encourage students to make a large mural of the associations they come up with. Display the mural in the classroom.

Acting Out Analogies with Paper-Plate Masks

Invite children to choose fairy tales or other favorite stories, such as "Little Red Riding Hood" and "Hansel and Gretel." Provide paper plates for the children and have them create masks of the main characters of each story. Then encourage children to create scenes illustrating the analogous relationships. For example, Little Red Riding Hood is to the big, bad wolf as Hansel and Gretel are to the witch.

Analogy Race

Divide the class into groups. Give each group the same list of familiar vocabulary words that can be used as analogies for one another. Then challenge the students to come up with a number of analogies using the words on the list. The first group to use all the words is the winner. Have the winning team share all of their analogies with the rest of the class.

Student's Name _____

Assessment Tool Progress Report

Progress

Improvement

Comments

Comprehension Strategies for an Integrated Language Arts Classroom © 1994 Fearon Teacher Aids

Practice 1

All of the pictures in the box are used as answers.

Example: is to as is to .

1. is to as is to _____ .

2.  is to as  is to _____ .

3. is to as is to _____ .

4. is to as is to _____ .

5. is to as is to _____ .

Comprehension Strategies for an Integrated Language Arts Classroom © 1994 Fearon Teacher Aids

Practice 2

All of the pictures in the box are used as answers.

Example: is to as is to .

1. is to as is to .

2. is to as is to .

3. is to as is to .

4. is to as is to .

5. is to  as is to .

Name _____

Practice 3

All of the pictures in the box are *not* used as answers.

Example: is to as is to _____ .

1. is to  as is to _____ .

2. is to as  is to _____ .

3. is to as is to _____ .

4. is to as is to _____ .

5. is to as is to _____ .

Practice 4

All of the pictures in the box are *not* used as answers.

Example: is to as is to .

1. is to  as is to .

2. is to as  is to .

3. is to as is to .

4. is to  as is to .

5. is to as is to .

Name _____

Practice 5

All of the pictures in the box are used as answers.

Example: Man is to  as boy is to  .

1. Go is to as stop is to   .

2. Face is to as tree is to   .

3. Round is to as pointed is to   .

4. Lion is to as elephant is to   .

5. Dry is to as wet is to   .

Name _____

Practice 6

All of the pictures in the box are *not* used as answers.

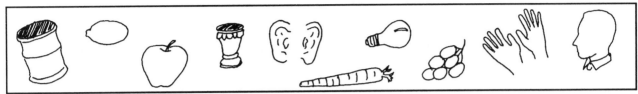

Example: Fruit is to as vegetable is to  .

1. See is to as hear is to _____ .

2. Walk is to as hold is to _____ .

3. Sweet is to as sour is to _____ .

4. Book is to PAGE as lamp is to _____ .

5. Milk is to QUART as oil is to _____ .

Name _____

Practice 7

All of the words in the box are used as answers.

| write   quack   dollar   yellow   finger   plane |

Example: is to dime as is to ___dollar___ .

1. is to boat as is to _____ .

2. is to bark as is to _____ .

3. is to ear as is to _____ .

4. is to blue as is to _____ .

5.  is to eat as  is to _____ .

Comprehension Strategies for an Integrated Language Arts Classroom © 1994 Fearon Teacher Aids

Name _____

Practice 8

All of the pictures in the box are *not* used as answers.

tires	tall	whoo	bray	quack	tame
mean	small	dig	hole	house	building
church	ten	fifty	hundred	egg	

Example: is to milk as is to _____egg_____.

1. is to oink as is to _____.

2.  is to hospital as is to _____.

3.  is to wild as 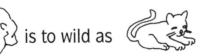 is to _____.

4. is to five as is to _____.

5. is to cut as  is to _____.

Practice 9

Directions: Below are sets of words that have a certain relationship to one another. Each set has a missing word that you need to supply. Look at the first pair of words. Try to figure out what the relationship is. Then choose a word from the word list that best completes the second pair in the set. All the words in the word list are used as answers. The first is done for you.

Word List: sentence, wolf, bed, story, knee, smell

1. Sit is to chair as lie is to _____ bed _____.

2. Mouth is to taste as nose is to _____.

3. Water is to shark as land is to _____.

4. Arm is to leg as elbow is to _____.

5. Sentence is to word as paragraph is to _____.

6. Sentence is to paragraph as paragraph is to _____.

Comprehension Strategies for an Integrated Language Arts Classroom © 1994 Fearon Teacher Aids

Name _____

Practice 10

Directions: Below are sets of words that have a certain relationship to one another. Each set has a missing word that you need to supply. Look at the first pair of words. Try to figure out what the relationship is. Then choose a word from the word list that best completes the second pair in the set. All the words in the word list are *not* used as answers. The first is done for you.

Word List: hide, house, nice, proud, bull, hay, sow, stallion, ewe, gander, drake, stable, water, milk, drink, cruel, tired, great, hot

1. Bird is to nest as horse is to _____ stable _____.

2. Cool is to cold as warm is to _____.

3. Cow is to bull as duck is to _____.

4. Deer is to doe as pig is to _____.

5. Hungry is to eat as thirsty is to _____.

6. In is to out as kind is to _____.

Name _____

Practice 11

Directions: Below are sets of words that have a certain relationship to one another. Each set has a missing word that you need to supply. Look at the first pair of words. Try to figure out what the relationship is. Then choose a word from the word list that best completes the second pair in the set. All the words in the word list are used as answers.

Word List: quiet, less, bean, cub, doe, always, yesterday, soft, young, weak

1. Night is to day as old is to _____.

2. Fruit is to plum as vegetable is to _____.

3. Black is to white as hard is to _____.

4. Cat is to kitten as bear is to _____.

5. Horse is to mare as deer is to _____.

6. Loud is to soft as noisy is to _____.

7. Wrong is to right as never is to _____.

8. Stop is to go as strong is to _____.

9. Most is to least as more is to _____.

10. Tomorrow is to today as today is to _____.

Comprehension Strategies for an Integrated Language Arts Classroom © 1994 Fearon Teacher Aids

Name _____

Practice 12

Directions: Below are sets of words that have a certain relationship to one another. Each set has a missing word that you need to supply. Look at the first pair of words. Try to figure out what the relationship is. Then choose a word from the word list that best completes the second pair in the set. All the words in the word list are used as answers.

Word List: nephew, buy, dollar, wheel, low, empty, eat, drake, toe, neigh

1. Up is to down as high is to _____.

2. Hand is to finger as foot is to _____.

3. Sister is to brother as niece is to _____.

4. Donkey is to bray as horse is to _____.

5. Chicken is to rooster as duck is to _____.

6. Penny is to dime as dime is to _____.

7. In is to out as sell is to _____.

8. Sit is to stand as full is to _____.

9. Milk is to drink as food is to _____.

10. Car is to tire as wagon is to _____.

Name _____

Practice 13

Directions: Below are sets of words that have a certain relationship to one another. Each set has a missing word that you need to supply. Look at the first pair of words. Try to figure out what the relationship is. Then choose a word from the word list that best completes the second pair in the set. All the words in the word list are *not* used as answers.

Word List: silk, vehicle, clothing, cold, eight, ten, cool, small, seven, moon, star, nickel, dime, dollar, quarter, dumb, lemon, even, wool, sour

1. Happy is to sad as hot is to _____.

2. Right is to wrong as odd is to _____.

3. Awake is to asleep as smart is to _____.

4. Sweet is to sour as candy is to _____.

5. Pliers is to tool as ship is to _____.

6. Quarter is to half-dollar as half-dollar is to _____.

7. Earth is to planet as sun is to _____.

8. Meat is to food as dress is to _____.

9. Bee is to honey as worm is to _____.

10. Fly is to six as spider is to _____.

Comprehension Strategies for an Integrated Language Arts Classroom © 1994 Fearon Teacher Aids

Name _____

Practice 14

Directions: Below are sets of words that have a certain relationship to one another. Each set has a missing word that you need to supply. Look at the first pair of words. Try to figure out what the relationship is. Then choose a word from the word list that best completes the second pair in the set. All the words in the word list are *not* used as answers.

Word List: sibling, child, nephew, niece, sister, city, depot, six, four, two, continent, thirsty, water, drink, mildew, talk, shout, hangar, excuse, tell, help, protect, mouse, ant, turtle, tired, rough, Africa

1. Car is to garage as plane is to _____.

2. Uncle is to aunt as brother is to _____.

3. China is to Asia as Egypt is to _____.

4. Triangle is to three as square is to _____.

5. Cotton is to soft as sandpaper is to _____.

6. Nap is to sleep as sip is to _____.

7. Friend is to pal as pardon is to _____.

8. Drizzle is to downpour as whisper is to _____.

9. Warm-blooded is to seal as cold-blooded is to _____.

10. Moisture is to rust as fungus is to _____.

Name _____

Practice 15

Directions: Below are sets of words that have a certain relationship to one another. Each set has a missing word that you need to supply. Look at the first pair of words. Try to figure out what the relationship is. Then choose a word from the word list that best completes the second pair in the set. All the words in the word list are *not* used as answers.

Word List: Mister, Sir, gun, triangle, one, Reverend, pupil, sleep, look, bite, Africa, South America, country, few, clean, tomorrow, today, before, still, two, six, four, feet, toes, Asia, city, yesterday, Sunday, Monday

1. Good is to bad as dirty is to _____.

2. Robin is to two as deer is to _____.

3. France is to Europe as Japan is to _____.

4. Country is to continent as state is to _____.

5. Ambassador is to Honorable as priest is to _____.

6. Present is to now as past is to _____.

7. One is to three as yard is to _____.

8. Quiver is to arrow as holster is to _____.

9. Finger is to nail as eye is to _____.

10. Today is to yesterday as tomorrow is to _____.

Comprehension Strategies for an Integrated Language Arts Classroom © 1994 Fearon Teacher Aids

Strategy 10:
Finding Inconsistencies

Explanation

Good thinkers are logical—that is, they are able to reason correctly. Finding inconsistencies refers to statements that do not make sense—they are illogical and not in accord with the given information. Finding inconsistencies in text is an important skill for students to learn. This skill helps students be alert while reading, learn to think logically, and question what they read.

Teaching Strategies in Action

Good readers are alert readers. Help your students recognize that everything that they read is not necessarily true or correct. If they read something that does not make sense, even if it is a textbook written by an authority in the field, they should question it.

Example:
If in a book about Mexico, students found the statement "There are approximately 10,000 people in Mexico City," should they believe it? Ask the students to reread the sentence. Does it make sense? Mexico City is the capital of Mexico. 10,000 people is not really a lot of people living in a capital city. No, it doesn't make sense. They must have meant 10,000,000.

Sample Practices

Here are some sample practices that you can use with your students.

1. The dog meowed at the mail carrier.

    This sentence is inconsistent. A dog doesn't meow. The writer must have meant "the dog barked."

2. There are a total of 20 states in the United States.

    The writer must have meant to write "50" instead of "20." 50 states make up the United States.

3. Ms. Jacob has 30 children in her park. At 2:30, all the children ran out to play in the class.

    This sentence does not make sense. If reread, one can see that the words "park" and "class" were switched. The sentence should read:

    Ms. Jacob has 30 children in her class. At 2:30, all the children ran out to play in the park.

Modeling Strategy

Here is how Ms. Evans, using a modeling strategy, helps her students recognize that good readers are alert readers.

Ms. Evans writes the following statement on the chalkboard:

Humans drink about 1,000 quarts of liquid in a week.

Ms. Evans asks her students to read the statement. Then she says "When I read this statement, it doesn't make sense to me. I keep rereading it because I think I have not read it correctly. I decide that the writer must have made a mistake. It doesn't make sense to me because I know there are only seven days in a week. Even if someone drank four quarts of liquid a day, which is a very large amount, that person would still only be drinking 28 quarts. I know that there are four large glasses of liquid in one quart. That means I would have to drink 16 large glasses of liquids in one day. That would be hard to do. But even if I were to do that, I still would only be drinking 28 quarts a week. To drink 1,000 quarts would mean I would be drinking 4,000 large glasses of liquid a week. That does not make any sense. The '1,000' is a mistake. The writer probably meant to say ten quarts."

Ms. Evans then writes the following sentence on the chalkboard. She asks the children to read it and tell her what they think about it.

The tame lion attacked the three men.

"Does it make sense to you?" she asks. "When I read the sentence," she continues, "it doesn't make sense to me because a tame lion would most likely not attack anyone. The writer probably meant to say *wild*. A wild animal would more likely attack people."

Learning Objective

To find inconsistencies in sentences or paragraphs and replace these with the correct word or words.

Directions for Student Practices

Use the student practices on pages 151-155 to help your students acquire, reinforce, and review finding inconsistencies. Pick and choose the practices based on the needs and developmental levels of your students. Answers for the student practice pages are on page 309.

When practicing finding inconsistencies, have the children read the directions and then answer the questions. For those who have difficulty reading, read the directions aloud to the children and orally ask them the questions.

Extensions

Sing a Simple Song

Invite the children to sing some familiar songs with you, such as "Twinkle, Twinkle, Little Star" or "Mary Had a Little Lamb." As you sing with the children, change one of the words in the chorus. The children will, of course, notice your blunder. Then ask the children to tell you the correct word.

Making Posters

Encourage students to find errors in stories, books, magazine articles, headlines, and so on. If possible, keep a small list of errors yourself. Once errors have been found, help students determine how the meanings of the sentences or paragraphs are changed by the errors. Then invite students to make posters of especially funny or absurd errors.

Changing Titles

Invite students to choose some of their favorite books or stories. Encourage children to change one word in each of the story titles that radically changes the meaning of the title into something funny or ridiculous. Students can then make up stories to go with their new titles.

Student's Name _____

Assessment Tool Progress Report

Progress

Improvement

Comments

Name _____

Practice 1

Directions: Read each sentence carefully. Find the word in each sentence that does not make sense. Replace that word with one from the word list that does make sense in the sentence. All the words in the word list are *not* used as answers.

Word List: night, bread, cold, hot, slippery, feathers, bones, falls, rises, stays

1. The ice was dry, so I fell.   _____

2. We had to pluck the scales off the chicken.   _____

3. The stars lit up the sky at noon.   _____

4. We like to eat bead and jam.   _____

5. In the morning, the sun sets.   _____

Name _____

Practice 2

Directions: Read each sentence carefully. Find the word in each sentence that does not make sense. Replace that word with one from the word list that does make sense in the sentence. All the words in the word list are *not* used as answers.

Word List: bottom, day, half-dollars, nickels, quarters, dusk, western, mine, cow, beard

1. I live in the eastern part of town, and my brother lives opposite me in the northern part of town. _____

2. At dawn, the sun sets. _____

3. The farmer milks the crow every morning. _____

4. My father gave me four dimes, which were just enough to buy one dollar's worth of paper and pencils. _____

5. His bear had grown so long that we did not know who he was. _____

Practice 3

Directions: Read each sentence carefully. Find the word in each sentence that does not make sense. Replace that word with one from the word list that does make sense in the sentence. All the words in the word list are *not* used as answers.

Word List: five, stag, sow, sugar, fine, wild, tender, three, chicks, pepper, doe

1. My mother won't let me have any tame pets.   _____

2. The hen looked proudly at her newborn ducklings.   _____

3. The mare led her deer family to safety.   _____

4. He put salt on his food to make it sweeter.   _____

5. At school, we always line up to go home when
   the clock strikes thee.   _____

Name _____

Practice 4

Directions: Read the short story carefully. Underline the words in the story that do not make sense. Choose words from the word list to replace the words that do not make sense. All the words in the word list are used as answers.

Word List: noisy, rooster, on, farm, five, morning, hen, crowing

A duck, a rooster, a hen, and five chicks lived together. They lived in a barn on a jungle. They stayed together all the time. Every evening, the hen would awaken everyone by blowing, "Cock-a-doodle-doo." The rooster would spend a lot of her time sitting in the eggs. The duck would play with the three chicks. It was always very quiet in the barn because they were always chattering.

1. _____   5. _____

2. _____   6. _____

3. _____   7. _____

4. _____   8. _____

Comprehension Strategies for an Integrated Language Arts Classroom © 1994 Fearon Teacher Aids

Practice 5

Directions: Read the short story carefully. Underline the words in the story that do not make sense. Choose words from the word list to replace the words that do not make sense. All the words in the word list are used as answers.

Word List: stopped, three, Mrs., her, stopped, kind, loud, sunny, noon, sun, many

Once upon a time, a hen took his three chicks for a walk. It was a nice, cloudy day. The moon was almost directly overhead. It was morning. At lunchtime, the streets are crowded. Few people were out for a walk. There were many cars, too. All of a sudden, there was a low noise. Everyone walked to look. There in the middle of the crowded street was Mrs. Hen and her four chicks. Mr. Hen had started traffic. A mean police officer went in the middle of the street. He helped Mrs. Hen and her chicks cross the street.

1. _____   6. _____

2. _____   7. _____

3. _____   8. _____

4. _____   9. _____

5. _____   10. _____

11. _____

Strategy 11:
Distinguishing Between Fact and Opinion

Explanation

The ability to differentiate between fact and opinion is a very important skill that students need to develop. Often, opinions are presented as though they are facts. Opinions are not facts. They are based on attitudes or feelings. Opinions can vary from individual to individual—they cannot be proven right or wrong conclusively. Facts, on the other hand, do not change from person to person. Facts can be proven to be true.

Teaching Strategies in Action

It is important to help your students as early as possible to determine whether information is factual or not. Present a picture to the children and ask them if they like it. After a number of children in the class have given their opinions, discuss with them how different children have different feelings about the picture. Point out to the children that they were giving their opinions about the picture and opinions may change from person to person.

Next, ask one child to tell you his or her name. Then call on other children in the class to give the name of that same child. Discuss with the children how everyone agrees on the child's name. Explain to the children that it's a fact that Mary Smith's name is Mary Smith. Tell children that something that is a fact does not change from person to person. Facts can be proven to be true.

Example:

Facts	Opinions
Albany is the capital of New York.	That is a pretty dress.
Twelve inches equals a foot.	He is very smart.
A meter equals 39.37 inches.	It's important to visit museums.

Sample Practices

Here are some sample practices that you can use with your students.

1. He has a nice smile. (opinion)

2. This chocolate cake tastes great! (opinion)

3. A horse has four legs. (fact)

4. All people are mammals. (fact)

5. I can call my friends on the telephone. (fact)

6. That clown's red nose makes him look silly. (opinion)

Modeling Strategy

Mrs. Brown presents the children with the following sentences. She tells the children that she will show them how she figures out whether something is a fact or an opinion.

Melissa is pretty.
Andrew is a good ball player.
The United States is a country.
Arithmetic is a school subject.
Baseball is fun.
Monday is a day of the week.
Ice cream tastes good.
Frank is a nice guy.

"I know," Mrs. Brown says, "that when something is an opinion, it can change from person to person. It cannot be proven to be right or wrong. If something is a fact, it does not change from person to person. It can be proven or shown to be true.

"When I read the statement 'Melissa is pretty,' I know the statement is an opinion because not everyone will agree with me. What I think is pretty, someone else may not think is pretty. Also, the statement 'Andrew is a good ball player' is an opinion. Even though I think he is a good ball player, not everyone agrees. It is my opinion. However, the sentence that says 'The United States is a country' is not an opinion. I know that statement is a fact. It can be proven to be true. Everyone agrees. We can all find information or evidence to prove it," says Mrs. Brown.

Mrs. Brown then goes over all the other sentences with the students and asks them to tell her whether each sentence is a fact or an opinion.

Learning Objective

To determine the difference between fact and opinion.

Directions for Student Practices

Use the student practices on pages 160-164 to help your students acquire, reinforce, and review distinguishing between fact and opinion. Pick and choose the practices based on the needs and developmental levels of your students. Answers for the student practice pages are on page 310.

When practicing distinguishing between fact and opinion, have the children read the directions and then answer the questions. For those who have difficulty reading, read the directions aloud to the children and orally ask them the questions.

Extensions

Bulletin Board

Make a "Fact or Opinion" bulletin-board display. Divide a bulletin board into two sections—one titled "Fact" and the other titled "Opinion." As students come across statements of fact or opinion in their reading, encourage students to write the statements on strips of paper. Then invite children to place the statements on the appropriate side of the bulletin board.

Character Containers

Invite children to choose a favorite book or story. As you read the story together with the class, have children keep track of the characters' opinions throughout the story. Write the opinions of each character on the chalkboard. Then give each child a covered oatmeal container and his or her choice of construction paper. Each child can draw the face of one of the characters on the lid of the oatmeal container. Help each child write that characters opinions on the construction paper and then glue the paper around the containers. Display the character containers in the classroom.

Book Reports

When the students are reading nonfiction and fiction books or stories, challenge students to list 5 of the most important facts they learned from their reading, as well as list 5 opinions that were stated in the book or story. You may want to provide book-report forms for the children to fill out as they read.

Student's Name _____

Assessment Tool Progress Report

Progress

Improvement

Comments

Name _____

Practice 1

Directions: Read each sentence carefully. Decide if the statement is a fact or if the statement is an opinion. Remember that if the statement is an opinion, then it can change from person to person. If the statement is a fact, it can't change. In front of each sentence, put the letter *O* if it's an opinion and the letter *F* if it's a fact.

_____   1. That picture is pretty.

_____   2. Parents work hard.

_____   3. Baseball is fun to play.

_____   4. Spelling is a school subject.

_____   5. An apple is a fruit.

Name _____

Practice 2

Directions: Read each sentence carefully. Decide if the statement is a fact or if the statement is an opinion. Remember that if the statement is an opinion, then it can change from person to person. If the statement is a fact, it can't change. In front of each sentence, put the letter *O* if it's an opinion and the letter *F* if it's a fact.

_____   1. Arithmetic is a hard subject.

_____   2. Milk is a dairy product.

_____   3. Sixty minutes equals an hour.

_____   4. This room is too hot.

_____   5. Kelsey is a good singer.

Name _____

Practice 3

Directions: Read each sentence carefully. Decide if the statement is a fact or if the statement is an opinion. Remember that if the statement is an opinion, then it can change from person to person. If the statement is a fact, it can't change. In front of each sentence, put the letter O if it's an opinion and the letter F if it's a fact.

_____   1. A turtle is able to live on land.

_____   2. Turtles are fun to own.

_____   3. Turtles are ugly.

_____   4. A turtle has a bony shell.

_____   5. A turtle is able to live in fresh water.

Comprehension Strategies for an Integrated Language Arts Classroom © 1994 Fearon Teacher Aids

Name _____

Practice 4

Directions: Read each sentence carefully. Decide if the statement is a fact or if the statement is an opinion. Remember that if the statement is an opinion, then it can change from person to person. If the statement is a fact, it can't change. In front of each sentence, put the letter O if it's an opinion and the letter F if it's a fact.

_____ 1. Television is fun to watch.

_____ 2. Game shows are better than talk shows.

_____ 3. A person can't fly like a bird.

_____ 4. Jogging is the best exercise.

_____ 5. Air is needed to live.

Name _____

Practice 5

Directions: Read each sentence carefully. Decide if the statement is a fact or if the statement is an opinion. Remember that if the statement is an opinion, then it can change from person to person. If the statement is a fact, it can't change. In front of each sentence, put the letter *O* if it's an opinion and the letter *F* if it's a fact.

_____ 1. Ice is frozen water.

_____ 2. History books are fun to read.

_____ 3. Food is needed in order to live.

_____ 4. Lemons taste good.

_____ 5. Fairy tales are fun to read.

Section Two

Vocabulary Expansion Skills

Developing Vocabulary Expansion Skills

Good vocabulary and good reading go hand in hand. Unless children know the meanings of words, they will have difficulty in understanding what they are reading. Without an understanding of words, comprehension is impossible.

As children advance in concept development, their vocabulary development must also advance—the two are interrelated. Children deficient in vocabulary will usually be deficient in concept development. That's why it is so important to build children's sight vocabulary as well as stress the vocabulary development that concerns the building of a larger word-meaning vocabulary.

Vocabulary Development and Individual Differences

For a vocabulary program to be successful, individual differences must be recognized among the amount and kinds of words that kindergarten and first-grade children have in their listening vocabulary (ability to understand a word when it is spoken). Some children come to school with a rich and varied vocabulary, whereas others have a more limited and narrow vocabulary. Some children may come to school with a rich and varied vocabulary that can be used with their peers and at home, but it may not be one that is very useful to them in school. For example, some children may possess a large lexicon of street vocabulary and expressions, and some others may speak a dialect of English that may contain its own special expressions and vocabulary.

Also be aware that a young child's listening vocabulary is larger than his or her speaking vocabulary and certainly larger than his or her reading and writing vocabulary. All four areas of vocabulary need to be developed. However, because a child first learns language through the aural-oral approach, begin with the listening and speaking areas first.

Vocabulary Consciousness

In the primary grades, children begin to come across words that are spelled the same but have different meanings based on their context in the sentence. For example, children learn that the word *saw* in "I saw Eddie" does not carry the same meaning as it does in "Sarah helped her dad saw the wood." When primary-grade children recognize that *saw, train, coat*, and many other words have different meanings based on surrounding words, children are beginning to build a vocabulary consciousness. This vocabulary consciousness grows when children begin asking about and looking up new words that they come across in their everyday activities.

As students become more advanced in reading, their vocabularies can be expanded in fun ways. One way to challenge primary-grade level children's budding vocabulary consciousness is to use word riddles or word activities (see Section Three). If children are fascinated with words, they will want to know the largest word in the dictionary, enjoy doing word games and puzzles, and have fun pronouncing funny or nonsense-sounding words. Help children to do the following:

1. Become aware of words they do not know.

2. Try to guess the meanings of words from the context.

3. Begin to learn word parts.

4. Jot down words that they do not know and look the words up in the dictionary later.

5. Keep a notebook and write down the words they have missed in their vocabulary exercises.

6. Maintain interest in wanting to expand vocabulary.

The practices in Section Two concern the building of vocabulary. A brief explanation of the vocabulary expansion skills that are present in this section follows:

Strategy 12	Using Context Clues to Determine Word Meanings	To figure out the meaning of a word from the surrounding words in the sentence.
Strategy 13	Expanding Vocabulary with Words That Have the Same or Nearly the Same Meaning (Synonyms) and Words That Are Opposite in Meaning (Antonyms)	To find and understand the difference in words that have the same or similar meanings (synonyms) and words that are opposite in meaning (antonyms).
Strategy 14	Expanding Vocabulary Using Words with Multiple Meanings (Homographs)	To figure out the meaning of words that are spelled the same but have different meanings based on how they are used in the sentence.

Strategy 12:
Using Context Clues to Determine Word Meanings

Explanation

Context clues help students determine the meanings of unfamiliar words. By *context,* we mean the words surrounding a word that can throw light on its meaning. A context clue is an item of information surrounding a particular word in the form of a definition, description, explanation, comparison, contrast, example, synonym, antonym, and so on.

Help students be aware of the various clues that writers give readers to understand the meaning of less familiar words. Some textbook writers will define, describe, or explain a word to make sure that readers understand the meaning. Other techniques that writers use include comparison and contrast, synonyms and antonyms (Strategy 13), examples, and more.

Teaching Strategies in Action

Help your students use context clues to figure out word meanings. Explain to the children that context clues are helpful in figuring out unfamiliar words in sentences. Share with the children that context clues are especially important in figuring out words with multiple meanings (Strategy 14). Present the following sentence to the children and see if they can figure out the meaning of the word *enormous*.

Example:
Jane's house was so *enormous* that we got lost in it.

From the context of the sentence, children should realize that the word *enormous* must mean "large" or "very big."

Sometimes children can actually determine the definition of a word from the sentence or from sentences that follow.

Example:
Darryl behaved in a very *rash* manner. He rushed in too quickly and was not very careful.

From the sentences, children should determine that the word *rash* refers to something that is done too quickly and not very carefully.

Alert readers can also use contrasts or comparisons to gain clues to meanings of words. Have your students try to determine the meaning of the word *prudent* in the following sentence.

Example:
Mary is usually a *prudent* person, but she was foolish yesterday.

If your students guessed *wise* for the meaning of *prudent*, they were correct. Students learn from the context clues that the word *prudent* is somehow the opposite of the word *foolish*. This is an example of contrasts.

In the next example, your students can see how comparisons can help them figure out the meaning.

Example:
Fred was as *obstinate* as a mule.

In this sentence, the word *obstinate* means "stubborn." A mule is an animal that is considered stubborn. By understanding the comparison, your students can get an idea of what *obstinate* means, even though it is a difficult word or one that they may not have seen before.

In the following sentence, your students can see how examples can help them figure out the meaning of a word.

Example::
The only *tools* I have are a hammer, saw, and wrench.

From the examples *hammer, saw*, and *wrench*, your students learn that a tool must be an instrument that you use to fix or make something.

In the following sentence, your students can see how the words *that is* signal that an explanation is to follow.

Example:
The story is incredible—*that is*, it is simply not believable.

Help your students to recognize that good readers use all these clues to help them determine word meanings.

Sample Practices

Here are some sample practices that you can use with your students.

1. The eagle *soared* over the tall trees.

   An eagle flies and these trees are tall, so the word *soared* must mean "to fly high."

2. Wanda wasn't very *considerate*. She wasn't thoughtful of the feelings of others.

   The word *considerate* means to be thoughtful of the feelings of others. The second sentence gives the clue.

3. Peter is as funny as a *comedian*.

   Peter is funny and Peter is as funny as a comedian, so the word *comedian* must mean a funny person.

4. I was famished—*that is*, I was very hungry.

   The words *that is* let students know there is an explanation—*famished* means "very hungry."

Modeling Strategy

Here is how Ms. Schneider helps the children learn to use context clues. She presents her students with the following sentences:

Mrs. Brown grows vegetables on her farm.
She grows peas, beans, corn, carrots, and beets.

Then Ms. Schneider says "Here is how I go about figuring out the meaning of the word *vegetables*. From reading the sentences, I see that there are a number of clues to help me figure out the meaning of the word *vegetables*. The clues are *peas, beans, corn, carrots*, and *beets*. The words *peas, beans, corn, carrots*, and *beets* are examples of vegetables. I know that examples are not the meaning of a word. An example is something that shows what the rest are like. Examples may not be the meaning of a word, but they can help us figure out word meanings. From the examples, I see that vegetables are parts of plants that we eat."

Then she says "Here are two other sentences. Let's see if we can figure out the meaning of the word *family* using examples as clues." Ms. Schneider puts the following two sentences on the chalkboard:

There are six people in my family.
My grandmother, mother, father, two brothers, and I live in our home.

"See if you do the same things I do. First I look for the clues. The clues are *six people, grandmother, mother, father, two brothers*, and *I*. The sentences do not give me the meaning of the word family, but they give me examples. The words *grandmother, mother, father, brothers*, and *I* are all examples and part of a family. Usually, families live together in the same home. From these examples, I see that these people are part of a family. They are all related and live together in the same home."

Learning Objective

To use a variety of context clues to determine the meanings of words.

Directions for Student Practices

Use the student practices on pages 173-187 to help your students acquire, reinforce, and review using context clues to determine word meanings. Pick and choose the practices based on the needs and developmental levels of your students. Answers for the student practice pages are on pages 310-311.

When practicing using context clues to determine word meanings, have the children read the directions and then answer the questions. For those who have difficulty reading, read the directions aloud to the children and orally ask them the questions.

Extensions

What Do You Think?

Encourage students to make note of new words in their reading that they have never seen before. Ask students to write definitions of the words based on the context clues. (You many want to preselect the words.) Then invite students to compare their definitions with definitions in the dictionary.

Vocabulary Challenge

Have each student find an unfamiliar word in their reading. Ask each student to first read the word aloud to the class, and then read the word in the context of the sentence. Invite the other students to decide if the meaning can be determined from the context, and, if so, what the meaning is. You may want to do this in small groups, especially if you have a wide range of reading abilities.

Vocabulary Quilt

Invite each child to choose a vocabulary word from a favorite story or book that they would like to illustrate. Provide squares of paper or muslin in whatever size you prefer, keeping in mind how large you want the finished quilt to be. Invite each child to write his or her vocabulary word on a square. Encourage children to also illustrate their vocabulary words with colorful markers. Help children write sentences using their vocabulary words as part of their designs. If you use paper squares, the squares can be taped to a large sheet of colored butcher paper and displayed on a wall in the classroom. If you use muslin, you can sew each child's design together to make a quilt.

Student's Name _____

Assessment Tool Progress Report

Progress

Improvement

Comments

Comprehension Strategies for an Integrated Language Arts Classroom © 1996 Fearon Teacher Aids

Name _____

Practice 1

Directions: Read each sentence carefully. Use context clues to help you choose the word that best fits the sentence. Put the word in the blank. All the words in the word list are used as answers.

Word List: rose, point, suit, box, play

1. That was a good _____ she made in the game.

2. The pitcher stood in the _____.

3. We _____ late yesterday.

4. That color does not _____ you.

5. What is the _____ of the story?

Name _____

Practice 2

Directions: Read each sentence carefully. Use context clues to help you choose the word that best fits the sentence. Put the word in the blank. All the words in the word list are used as answers.

Word List: run, rest, pitch, bear, strike

1. It was _____ black last night.

2. The movie will _____ for two weeks.

3. The workers went on _____.

4. Leave the _____ for me.

5. Tell them to _____ left.

Comprehension Strategies for an Integrated Language Arts Classroom © 1994 Fearon Teacher Aids

Name _____

Practice 3

Directions: Read each sentence carefully. Use context clues to help you choose the word that best fits the sentence. Put the word in the blank. All the words in the word list are used as answers.

Word List: iron, monkey, lamb, plum, plant

1. My father works in a(n) _____.

2. What a(n) _____ that job is. It is so easy.

3. They tricked the man and made a(n) _____ out of him.

4. He is as tame as a(n) _____.

5. They will try to _____ out the problems.

Name _____

Practice 4

Directions: Read each sentence carefully. Use context clues to help you choose the word that best fits the sentence. Put the word in the blank. All the words in the word list are used as answers.

Word List: broke, break, fast, pinch, flowed

1. During the _____ , I met my friend.

2. On Fridays, I am always _____.

3. The crowd _____ through the gate.

4. I always feel the money _____ on Fridays.

5. After being on a(n) _____, I was starved.

Comprehension Strategies for an Integrated Language Arts Classroom © 1994 Fearon Teacher Aids

Practice 5

Directions: Read each sentence carefully. Use context clues to help you choose the word that best tells the feelings of the person in the sentence. Put the word in the blank. All the words in the word list are used as answers. A word may be used only once.

Word List: sad, sick, tired, good, silly

1. When my kitten was hurt, I felt _____.

2. Jake felt _____ when he saw that he was wearing one red sock and one blue sock.

3. After eating too much, Jack felt _____.

4. Carol felt _____ when she was invited to the party.

5. Serena was _____ after working hard all day.

Name _____

Practice 6

Directions: Read each sentence carefully. Use context clues to help you choose the word that best tells the feelings of the person in the sentence. Put the word in the blank. All the words in the word list are used as answers. A word may be used only once.

Word List: angry, ashamed, proud, happy, insulted

1. Sharon was _____ when she saw a big boy hitting a little boy.

2. Chad was _____ when his sister won a prize.

3. Leanne was _____ when she was not invited to the party.

4. Greg was _____ that he had lied to his best friend.

5. Arthur was _____ when his parents bought him a bicycle.

Practice 7

Directions: Read each sentence carefully. Use context clues to help you choose the word that best tells the feelings of the person in the sentence. Put the word in the blank. All the words in the word list are used as answers. A word may be used only once.

Word List: embarrassed, guilty, peculiar, scared, joyful

1. Teresa was _____ when the sleeve of her dress tore when she raised her arm.

2. We were _____ when we saw the big dog coming toward us.

3. We felt _____ when all our tests were over.

4. Bart felt _____ about leaving all the work for the others to do.

5. Jim felt _____ about the situation and didn't know how to act.

Name _____

Practice 8

Directions: Read each sentence carefully. Use the context clues to help you figure out the meaning of the underlined word. Sometimes the clue to the word meaning is in the second sentence. Put the meaning of the underlined word in the blank.

1. It is <u>difficult</u> for me to climb a rope. _____

2. It seemed <u>incredible</u> that he could do all that work in one hour. _____

3. Jennifer will play a <u>dual</u> role in the play. She will play both a child and an old lady. _____

4. The doctors said that they had no quick <u>remedy</u> for the child's illness.
_____

5. The material was so <u>coarse</u> that it hurt my skin. _____

Comprehension Strategies for an Integrated Language Arts Classroom © 1994 Fearon Teacher Aids

Name _____

Practice 9

Directions: Read each sentence carefully. Use the context clues to help you figure out the meaning of the underlined word. Sometimes the clue to the word meaning is in the second sentence. Put the meaning of the underlined word in the blank.

1. My kitten is very tame. She will not hurt anyone. _____

2. Everyone knows her, because she is a famous writer. _____

3. That is such an enormous ice-cream cone. You will have to eat some of it. _____

4. We can all walk side by side on that street because it is ten feet broad. _____

5. The lion is a fierce animal. _____

6. The elephant is a huge animal. _____

7. The valiant knight fought the dragon. _____

8. The drug was so potent that it knocked out a six-foot-tall man. _____

9. After the fire demolished their house, the Browns had no place to live. _____

10. Mr. Smith gave both boys equivalent jobs to do. They both had to take care of the plants. _____

Name _____

Practice 10

Directions: Each sentence contains a nonsense word. Read each sentence carefully. Choose a word that you think makes sense in place of the nonsense word. Put the word in the blank. You may choose any word you like. The word, however, must make sense in the sentence.

1. I like to freble _____ with my kitten.

2. My father took us on a booble _____ ride.

3. On the farm, we saw a deeble _____ sitting on her eggs.

4. Next fromen, _____ we are going to visit my grandmother.

5. My greib _____ and I are going swimming.

6. At the loim, _____ we saw a funny-looking animal.

7. Who grammed _____ that?

8. I like to drebe _____.

9. Wurit _____ is my favorite food.

10. At the hoteim, _____ we are not allowed to do that.

Comprehension Strategies for an Integrated Language Arts Classroom © 1994 Fearon Teacher Aids

Name _____

Practice 11

Directions: Each sentence contains a nonsense word. Read each sentence carefully. Choose a word that you think makes sense in place of the nonsense word. Put the word in the blank. You may choose any word you like. The word, however, must make sense in the sentence.

1. My brother, <u>Sentle</u>, _____ and I went to the beach.

2. No one wants to <u>liert</u> _____ anymore.

3. At <u>verter</u>, _____ we have lots of fun.

4. After school, we played <u>meint</u> _____.

5. When I'm hot, I go <u>reinting</u> _____.

6. Please <u>neim</u> _____ that for me.

7. <u>Leiper</u> _____ helped the poor little dog.

8. A <u>brite</u> _____ was stuck in the tree.

9. The <u>hert</u> _____ is coming to town soon.

10. The <u>poiter</u> _____ frightened me.

Name _____

Practice 12

Directions: The following is a short story with scrambled words. Read each sentence carefully. Use context clues to help you figure out the scrambled words. Unscramble the words and put the correct words in the blanks below the story.

The Mouse in the House

I have a mouse that lives in my house. The soume[1] that lives ni[2] my house si[3] very msatr.[4] I like ti.[5] I vegi[6] it hescee[7] to eat. I lpay[8] dehi[9] and eeks[10] with it. I like hte[11] mouse that lives in my seouh.[12]

1. _____   7. _____

2. _____   8. _____

3. _____   9. _____

4. _____   10. _____

5. _____   11. _____

6. _____   12. _____

Comprehension Strategies for an Integrated Language Arts Classroom © 1994 Fearon Teacher Aids

Name _____

Practice 13

Directions: The following is a short story with scrambled words. Read each sentence carefully. Use context clues to help you figure out the scrambled words. Unscramble the words and put the correct words in the blanks below the story.

The Cat in the Tree

One day my cat ran up a tree. It <u>saw</u>[1] a very big <u>reet</u>.[2] My <u>tac</u>[3] sat on a <u>rbacnh</u>[4] of the tree. She <u>tas</u>[5] and <u>tas</u>[6] and <u>tas</u>.[7] We tried <u>ot</u>[8] get her to come <u>nwod</u>.[9] She just said "<u>eowm</u>."[10] She sat in the <u>reet</u>[11] all <u>ghtin</u>.[12] In the <u>nomring</u>,[13] <u>hes</u>[14] still sat in the tree. We did <u>ton</u>[15] know <u>htaw</u>[16] to do. Just then, <u>ew</u>[17] heard a <u>oudl</u>[18] noise. It frightened <u>ym</u>[19] cat. She <u>nar</u>[20] down the tree.

1. _____   11. _____

2. _____   12. _____

3. _____   13. _____

4. _____   14. _____

5. _____   15. _____

6. _____   16. _____

7. _____   17. _____

8. _____   18. _____

9. _____   19. _____

10. _____   20. _____

Name _____

Practice 14

Directions: The following is a short story with scrambled words. Read each sentence carefully. Use context clues to help you figure out the scrambled words. Unscramble the words and put the correct words in the blanks below the story.

Making New Friends

It is hard for me to make new friends. I am a hys[1] person. I ma[2] also very quiet. On[3] one really notices em.[4] I never know hawt[5] to yas.[6] In hscool,[7] I never raise my dahn.[8] I verne[9] keasp.[10] I do ton[11] like to eb[12] shy. I am not evry[13] happy. I would like to vahe[14] lots of refinds.[15]

1. _____   8. _____

2. _____   9. _____

3. _____   10. _____

4. _____   11. _____

5. _____   12. _____

6. _____   13. _____

7. _____   14. _____

15. _____

Comprehension Strategies for an Integrated Language Arts Classroom © 1994 Fearon Teacher Aids

Practice 15

Directions: The following is a short story with scrambled words. Read each sentence carefully. Use context clues to help you figure out the scrambled words. Unscramble the words and put the correct words in the blanks below the story.

The Animal Cookie

One day a little girl baked a little cookie. The keicoo[1] was a funny ttleil[2] bunny. It dah[3] gib[4] ears and a cute little lait.[5] The little grli[6] liked her cookie. Just sa[7] she saw[8] about to eat her little ynnbu,[9] she heard a voice yas[10] "Little girl, do ton[11] tea[12] me. Please od[13] not eat em."[14] The little lirg[15] looked around. There was on[16] one there. "Oolk[17] at me. Look ta[18] me," the voice said. The little girl deoolk[19] at the ooceik.[20] The cookie was inglatk![21] "I won't tea[22] you," said the little girl. Just then hte[23] little bunny hopped off the batle[24] and pohped[25] away. The little girl nar[26] after the cookie, tub[27] she could not tacch[28] the cookie. The nnuby[29] was too saft[30] for her.

1. _____   11. _____   21. _____

2. _____   12. _____   22. _____

3. _____   13. _____   23. _____

4. _____   14. _____   24. _____

5. _____   15. _____   25. _____

6. _____   16. _____   26. _____

7. _____   17. _____   27. _____

8. _____   18. _____   28. _____

9. _____   19. _____   29. _____

10. _____   20. _____   30. _____

Strategy 13: Expanding Vocabulary with Words That Have the Same or Nearly the Same Meaning (Synonyms) and Words That Are Opposite in Meaning (Antonyms)

Explanation

Synonyms and antonyms are often used by writers to enhance their writing. A *synonym* is a word with the same or nearly the same meaning. An *antonym* is a word that is opposite in meaning. By teaching children about synonyms and antonyms through examples as well as through the context of their own reading, you can help expand children's vocabulary significantly.

Because synonyms and antonyms are excellent context clues that writers use often, a special section is devoted to these two very important clues.

Teaching Strategies in Action

Synonyms are words that have the same or nearly the same meaning. Often, words may be defined by other words that are similar in meaning. The similar word that is used is often a word that is more familiar or more commonly used.

> *Examples:*
> *Indolent* is defined as "lazy."
> *Dire* is defined as "extreme."
> *Famished* is defined as "starved."
> *Valiant* is defined as "brave."

Antonyms are words opposite in meaning to others. Often, words may also be defined by other words of opposite and more familiar meaning.

> *Examples:*
> *Reluctant* is the opposite of "willing."
> *Significant* is the opposite of "unimportant."
> *Complex* is the opposite of "simple."

Help your students recognize that writers use synonyms and antonyms to make their writing clearer, more expressive, more informative, and more interesting.

Sample Practices

Here are some sample practices that you can use with your students.

Have your students generate either synonyms or antonyms for the underlined words in the sentences below.

1. The boat <u>drifted</u> on the water.

   Synonym: floated

2. Sheila <u>invented</u> a new dance.

   Synonym: created

3. Barbara was very <u>loud</u>.

   Antonym: quiet

4. Paul turned <u>up</u> the music.

   Antonym: down

Modeling Strategy

Here is how Mrs. Green helps her students use antonyms and synonyms to figure out word meanings. Mrs. Green has worked with the children to understand the concept of opposites. The children can give her the opposites of *tall, big, high, hard, thin, cruel,* and many other words as well. Mrs. Green puts the following sentence on the chalkboard and asks her students to tell her the meaning of the word *intelligent*:

Andrew is *intelligent* but his pal Jim is dumb.

"Here is what I do to figure out the meaning of the word *intelligent*," Mrs. Green says. "I read the sentence. I notice the word *but*. The word *but* is a signal that a contrast or an opposite follows. I know what the word *dumb* means. *Dumb* means "not smart." The opposite of *intelligent* is "not smart." Therefore, the word *intelligent* must mean "smart."

Mrs. Green presents her students with another sentence and has the children try to figure out the meaning of *frigid*.

Yesterday it was *frigid* but today it is hot.

Children should be able to state that the word *frigid* is the opposite of the word *hot*; therefore, *frigid* means not "hot" but "cold."

Mrs. Green also helps the children figure out word meanings using words with similar meanings (synonyms). She writes the following sentence on the chalkboard that contains an unfamiliar word. Mrs. Green then verbalizes her thoughts in figuring out the meaning of the unfamiliar word.

Sharon said that she felt ill after eating *rancid* or spoiled food.

Mrs. Green says "I see the word *or* in the sentence. Often the word *or* is used by the writer when he or she uses another word with a similar meaning. I don't know what the word *rancid* means, but I do know what the word *spoiled* means. It means "rotten" or "bad." *Spoiled* is similar in meaning to *rancid*. So *rancid* must mean "spoiled." (If the term *rancid* is used with your upper primary-grade children, make sure they understand that we talk about *rancid food*. Remind children that the term *rancid* does not refer to children.)

Learning Objective

To find words that have the same or nearly the same meaning as well as words with opposite meanings.

Directions for Student Practices

Use the student practices on pages 192-201 to help your students acquire, reinforce, and review synonyms and antonyms. Pick and choose the practices based on the needs and developmental levels of your students. Answers for the student practice pages are on page 312.

When practicing synonyms and antonyms, have the children read the directions and then answer the questions. For those who have difficulty reading, read the directions aloud to the children and orally ask them the questions.

Extensions

Make a Game

Divide the class into small groups and have each group design a simple game board based on a favorite story or book. Each game board should include a trail with a start and finish. Have children mark spaces throughout the trail with the words *synonym* and *antonym*. Write vocabulary words on cards. Students can use spinners or dice to determine how many spaces to move. A player spins or rolls the dice and moves the number of spaces indicated. He or she then takes the top vocabulary card and reads it aloud. If he or she has landed on a *synonym* space, then he or she must think of a synonym for the vocabulary word. The same is true for spaces marked *antonym*. The first player to reach the finish wins.

Finding Synonyms and Antonyms

Encourage students to look for sentences in their reading that use pairs of synonyms or antonyms in the same sentence. Have students write the sentences on long strips of paper and then pin the strips on a bulletin board. Then invite students to take turns finding synonyms or antonyms in the sentences written by their classmates.

Synonym and Antonym Pillows

Invite children to select synonym or antonym pairs to illustrate on pillows. Provide large muslin squares for the pillows. Provide markers, fabric paints, or fabric crayons for the illustrations. (Using fabric paints or fabric crayons will make the pillows washable. Follow the directions on the box.) Give each child two pieces of muslin—one of each word in their pairs of synonyms or antonyms. Encourage children to illustrate each of the words in the pair— one word on each piece of muslin. Help children put the illustrated sides of the fabric together and hand-stitch or machine-sew around 3 sides. Then show the children how to turn the fabric right-side out and stuff the inside with batting. Help children sew the openings closed.

Assessment Tool Progress Report

Progress

Improvement

Comments

Practice 1

Directions: Read each sentence carefully. Then read the words in the word list. Choose a word from the word list that is the same or almost the same as the underlined word in each sentence. Put the word in the blank. All the words in the word list are used as answers.

Word List: joyful, bright, ill, handsome, big

1. That is a <u>large</u> house. _____

2. The baby is <u>sick</u>. _____

3. He is a <u>happy</u> man. _____

4. I like <u>smart</u> people. _____

5. Scott is <u>good-looking</u>. _____

Practice 2

Directions: Read each sentence carefully. Then read the words in the word list. Choose a word from the word list that is the same or almost the same as the underlined word in each sentence. Put the word in the blank. All the words in the word list are used as answers.

Word List: mean, lady, thin, littie, correct

1. The <u>small</u> dog is cute. _____

2. Your answer is not <u>right</u>. _____

3. She is a <u>nasty</u> person. _____

4. The <u>woman</u> wore a blue outfit. _____

5. Jim is too <u>skinny</u>. _____

Name _____

Practice 3

Directions: Read each sentence carefully. Then read the words in the word list. Choose a word from the word list that is the same or almost the same as the underlined word in each sentence. Put the word in the blank. All the words in the word list are *not* used as answers.

Word List: cut, rope, rip, place, picture, spirit, price, game, ripe, pal, stuck, struck, spend, champ

1. What is the <u>cost</u> of that? _____

2. My <u>friend</u> is very nice. _____

3. I have a big <u>tear</u> in my sleeve. _____

4. He <u>hit</u> the ball hard. _____

5. That is a beautiful <u>spot</u>. _____

Comprehension Strategies for an Integrated Language Arts Classroom © 1994 Fearon Teacher Aids

Name _____

Practice 4

Directions: Read each sentence carefully. Then read the words in the word list. Choose a word from the word list that is the same or almost the same as the underlined word in each sentence. Put the word in the blank. All the words in the word list are *not* used as answers.

Word List: healthy, worthy, many, stupid, finish, wealthy, moist, dry, dump, poor

1. My friend is <u>rich</u>. _____

2. How can you be so <u>dumb</u>? _____

3. That is <u>damp</u>. _____

4. I hope my dog is <u>well</u>. _____

5. We will <u>end</u> the game soon. _____

Practice 5

Directions: Read each sentence carefully. Then read the words in the word list. Choose a word from the word list that is the same or almost the same as the underlined word in each sentence. Put the word in the blank. All the words in the word list are *not* used as answers.

Word List: dark, dull, damage, end, near, start, aid, chum, brother, scent, perfume, wide, trouble, hold, bottom, head, defend, star, line, clever

1. She is a <u>bright</u> student. _____

2. Let's <u>begin</u> the game now. _____

3. He is a good <u>buddy</u>. _____

4. My cat is at the <u>top</u> of the stairs. _____

5. My friend needs <u>help</u>. _____

6. When will you <u>finish</u> the game? _____

7. I will try to <u>protect</u> you. _____

8. That is a lovely <u>odor</u>. _____

9. What <u>harm</u> did the dog do to the house? _____

10. Did you go to a lot of <u>effort</u> to do that? _____

Comprehension Strategies for an Integrated Language Arts Classroom © 1994 Fearon Teacher Aids

Practice 6

Directions: Read each sentence carefully. Then read the words in the word list. Choose a word from the word list that is opposite in meaning to the underlined word in the sentence. Put the word in the blank. All the words in the word list are used as answers.

Word List: low, tall, back, little, later

1. He is a <u>short</u> man. _____

2. The kitten is <u>big</u>. _____

3. That is too <u>high</u>. _____

4. The teacher will talk to you <u>now</u>. _____

5. That is the <u>front</u> of the dress. _____

Name _____

Practice 7

Directions: Read each sentence carefully. Then read the words in the word list. Choose a word from the word list that is opposite in meaning to the underlined word in the sentence. Put the word in the blank. All the words in the word list are used as answers.

Word List: beautiful, clean, asleep, good, well

1. I feel <u>sick</u>. _____

2. He is a <u>bad</u> puppy. _____

3. The room is <u>dirty</u>. _____

4. The picture is <u>ugly</u>. _____

5. She is <u>awake</u>. _____

Comprehension Strategies for an Integrated Language Arts Classroom © 1994 Fearon Teacher Aids

Practice 8

Directions: Read each sentence carefully. Then read the words in the word list. Choose a word from the word list that is opposite in meaning to the underlined word in the sentence. Put the word in the blank. All the words in the word list are used as answers.

Word List: guilty, old, empty, sad, stale

1. She is <u>happy</u>. _____

2. The drawer is <u>full</u>. _____

3. That bat is <u>new</u>. _____

4. That bread is <u>fresh</u>. _____

5. She is <u>innocent</u>. _____

Practice 9

Directions: Each sentence below has two missing words. The missing words are opposite in meaning. Complete each sentence with word opposites that make sense in the sentence.

Example: If you eat too much, you may become too_____, but if you eat too little, you may become too_____.

Answers: fat; thin.

1. A giant is _____, but a dwarf is _____.

2. Sandpaper is _____, but cotton is _____.

3. When you play a game, you want to _____ , not _____.

4. When the sun _____, it's dawn, and when the sun _____, it's dusk.

5. The rain makes you _____, and the sun makes you _____.

Comprehension Strategies for an Integrated Language Arts Classroom © 1994 Fearon Teacher Aids

Name _____

Practice 10

Directions: Each sentence below has four missing words. The missing words are two pairs of word opposites. Read the words in the word list. Complete each sentence with word opposites from the word list that make sense in the sentence. All the words in the word list are *not* used as answers.

Word List: kind, play, awake, never, love, asleep, night, happy, always, day, hate, sad, help, sister, father, aunt, cousin, bad, brother, hurt, weak, cry, stay, healthy, pay, strong, niece, sick, laugh, cruel

Example: John is _____ when he _____ a game, but he is _____ when he_____.

Answers: sad, loses; happy, wins.

1. You may _____ when you are _____, and you may _____ when you are _____.

2. You are usually _____ during the _____, and you are usually _____ during the _____.

3. You are _____ when you are _____, and you are _____ when you are _____.

4. When you are _____, people _____ you, but when you are _____, people _____ you.

5. My _____ is _____ late, but my _____ is _____ late.

Strategy 14: Expanding Vocabulary Using Words with Multiple Meanings (Homographs)

Explanation

Words that are spelled the same but have different meanings are called *homographs*. Because many words have more than one meaning, you can help students recognize that the meaning of a particular word is determined by its use in a sentence.

Some homographs are spelled the same but do not sound the same.

> *Example:*
> 1. During the garbage strike, there were tons of uncollected *refuse* on the streets of the city.
>
> 2. I *refuse* to go along with you.

The word *refuse* means "trash." *Refuse* means "to decline to accept." In sentence 1, *refuse* (ref' use), meaning "trash," is pronounced differently from the term *refuse* (re fuse'), meaning "to decline to accept" in sentence 2. In reading, you can determine the meaning of *refuse* from the way it is used in the sentence (context clues).

To avoid confusion, all of the practices in this strategy section will present words with multiple meanings that are spelled the same and sound the same. These homographs are easier for children to work with.

Special Note

You may want to use the term *words with multiple meanings* with the students rather than *homographs*. You might introduce the term *homograph* to some of your older students.

Teaching Strategies in Action

Because many words have more than one meaning, the meaning of a particular word is determined by the position (syntax) of the word in a sentence and from meaning (semantic) clues of the surrounding words. Help your students be careful using these words with multiple meanings correctly.

> *Example:*
> "It wasn't fair that Harry got to go to the fair and I didn't."

Here, the word *fair* is spelled the same and sounds the same. But the meaning of the word *fair* is different in each case.

Sample Practices

Here are some sample practices that you can use with your students.

1. Use of the word *present*:

a. Terry brought a present to Josh's birthday party.

b. Phil was present at the meeting.

Explain to students that in the first sentence, the word *present* means "gift." In the second sentence, it means "at hand" or "in existence."

2. Use of the word *spring*.

a. Spring is finally here!

b. Joanne walks with a spring in her step.

Point out to children that the word *spring* in the first sentence refers to the season. *Spring* in the second sentence means "bounce" or "step lightly."

Modeling Strategy

Here is how Mr. Dupre helps the children work with words with multiple meanings (homographs). He writes the following pairs of sentences on the chalkboard.

1. The dogs *bark* at night.

2. The *bark* of the tree is peeling.

1. The *train* had a lot of people in it.

2. Did you *train* your dog to do that?

Mr. Dupre then says "What do you notice about these sentences? I notice that there are two sets of sentences. In each set, there is one word that is spelled the same. However, when I read each sentence in the set, I see that the same word means something different in each sentence. Let me see, in the first sentence of the first set, the word *bark* is an action word (a verb). It tells what the dog is doing. It tells what sound the dog is making. In the second sentence, the word *bark* is a naming word (a noun). It refers to the tough outer covering of a tree."

Mr. Dupre continues. "For the second set of words, I see that *train* is a naming word in the first sentence. It is a connected line of railroad cars that brings people from one place to another. In the second sentence, *train* is an action word. It means 'to teach.'

"It's the other words in the sentences that help me figure out the correct meanings of *bark* and *train*. The position of *bark* and *train*—that is, where the word is in the sentence—helps me figure out the meaning of each word."

Mr. Dupre then invites the children to practice working with words with multiple meanings. "Now that you have seen how I figure out the meanings of words that are spelled the same, here are some practices that will challenge you to do the same. Later on, we can make up some word riddles using words that are spelled the same but have different meanings."

Learning Objective

To figure out the meanings of words that are spelled the same but have different meanings based on how each word is used in the sentence.

Directions for Student Practices

Use the student practices on pages 207-216 to help your students acquire, reinforce, and review words with multiple meanings (homographs). Pick and choose the practices based on the needs and developmental levels of your students. Answers for the student practice pages are on page 313.

When practicing using words with multiple meanings, have the children read the directions and then answer the questions. For those who have difficulty reading, read the directions aloud to the children and orally ask them the questions.

Special Note

The presented homograph practices can be done in small groups or with the entire class, as well as individually. If children work individually on the homograph practices, it would help to go over the answers together in a group to encourage discussion and interaction.

Extensions

Two-Faced Puzzles

Invite each child to illustrate a word with multiple meanings on an 8 1/2" x 11"posterboard. On the other side of the posterboard, he or she can illustrate another meaning for the word. Then help each child cut the illustrated posterboard into puzzle pieces. Store each puzzle in a plastic zip-lock bag. Write the word illustrated on a piece of masking tape and label each bag.

Concentration Card Game

Have students write down words with multiple meanings they encounter in their reading. Provide blank index cards for the children and invite them to illustrate each word on two separate cards, using one meaning of the word on one card and the other meaning of the word on the other card. Then have children include an appropriate caption for each card using the word in a sentence. For example, using the word *plant*, a child may want to draw a plant on one card with the sentence "This is my green *plant*." On the other card, he or she might draw a picture of the plant in a garden with the sentence "I think I will *plant* my *plant* in my garden." Then children can use the sets of words with multiple meanings for a concentration card game. Place sets of cards, in scrambled order, face down on a table or the floor.

Each player, in turn, flips two cards up. If they make a set of words with multiple meanings, they keep these cards. If not, the cards are turned face down again, and it's the next person's turn. The winner is the child with the most card sets.

Funny Stories and Silly Poems

Invite students to make lists of words with multiple meanings that they find in their reading. Each child can then make a "word bank" of homographs to use to write funny stories or silly poems. Display stories and poems in the classroom.

Assessment Tool Progress Report

Progress

Improvement

Comments

Comprehension Strategies for an Integrated Language Arts Classroom © 1994 Fearon Teacher Aids

Practice 1

Directions: Read each sentence carefully. Choose a word from the word list that fits the blanks of the sentence and makes sense. Each word in the word list has different meanings but is spelled the same. All the words in the word list are used as answers. The first is done for you.

Word List: fall, train, pet, bark, can

1. I __can__ carry that heavy __can__ of beans.

2. My dog will _____ if you pick the _____ off the tree.

3. I need to _____ my dog not to bark when he hears the _____.

4. During the _____, the leaves begin to _____ in some parts of the country.

5. My _____ doesn't like you to _____ it too much.

Practice 2

Directions: Read each sentence carefully. Choose a word from the word list that fits the blanks of the sentence and makes sense. Each word in the word list has different meanings but is spelled the same. All the words in the word list are used as answers. The first is done for you.

Word List: fan, swing, well, spring, plant

1. It's fun to __swing__ on the __swing__.

2. In the _____ , I saw a fish _____ out of the _____.

3. The cat didn't feel _____ when it fell in the _____ and got all wet.

4. We will _____ a(n) _____ in our yard that will grow very tall.

5. On a hot day, I use my little _____ to _____ myself.

Comprehension Strategies for an Integrated Language Arts Classroom © 1994 Fearon Teacher Aids

Practice 3

Directions: Read each sentence carefully. Choose a word from the word list that fits the blanks of the sentence and makes sense. Each word in the word list has different meanings but is spelled the same. All the words in the word list are *not* used as answers. The first is done for you.

Word List: trail, march, saddle, grade, farm, tree, groom, fair, pass, pat, park, case, four

1. I needed a(n) __pass__ to __pass__ through the gate.

2. The _____ said that he would _____ the horse for his bride.

3. My mother wanted to _____ the car and then go for a walk in the _____.

4. I am in third _____ and I always get a good _____ in social studies.

5. We went to the _____ on a(n) _____ day and we had lots of fun there.

Practice 4

Directions: Read each sentence carefully. Choose a word from the word list that fits the blanks of the sentence and makes sense. Each word in the word list has different meanings but is spelled the same. All the words in the word list are *not* used as answers.

Word List: play, help, show, team, well, fine, group, band, ring, spell, batted, hit, class, glass

1. We needed to _____ our tickets to get into the _____.

2. My father did not feel _____ when he paid the parking _____.

3. The witch put a(n) _____ on anyone who could not _____.

4. When he _____ a home run, he made a(n) _____ with the fans.

5. The person in the _____ wore a(n) _____ around his head when he played the piano.

Comprehension Strategies for an Integrated Language Arts Classroom ® 1994 Fearon Teacher Aids

Practice 5

Directions: Read each sentence carefully. Choose a word from the word list that fits the blanks of the sentence and makes sense. Each word in the word list has different meanings but is spelled the same. All the words in the word list are *not* used as answers.

Word List: flower, cap, pitch, rose, pin, point, run, skip, jack, sock, hose, show

1. My sister _____ early in the morning to water her _____.

2. The garden _____ made my mother's _____ wet.

3. The teacher used a stick with a sharp _____ to _____ something out to us.

4. My brother used a(n) _____ to _____ up his car.

5. When the mower refused to _____ , I had to _____ to the store to buy a part for it.

Comprehension Strategies for an Integrated Language Arts Classroom © 1994 Fearon Teacher Aids

Practice 6

Directions: Read each sentence carefully. Think of a word that is spelled the same but has different meanings that fits the blanks of the sentence and makes sense. Put the word in the blanks. The first is done for you.

1. Everyone __present__ received a(n) __present__ .

2. The _____ in the pond likes to _____ its head in the water.

3. Use the _____ to _____ together the torn hem.

4. My new _____ had a(n) _____ of paint on its sleeve.

5. The gold _____ is _____, and it will make me very rich.

Comprehension Strategies for an Integrated Language Arts Classroom © 1994 Fearon Teacher Aids

Practice 7

Directions: Read each sentence carefully. Think of a word that is spelled the same but has different meanings that fits the blanks of the sentence and makes sense. Put the word in the blanks. The first is done for you.

1. I get a tan when I ___sun___ myself in the ___sun___ .

2. The _____ of the land said that he needed a(n) _____ to measure something.

3. They use a checkered _____ to _____ the race cars down when they come into the home stretch.

4. At the _____, the princess was given a large, round _____.

5. My brother will not eat _____ because he is very short, and everyone calls him a(n) _____.

6. The children stood in _____ to buy a fishing _____.

7. He spun the _____ on _____ of the table.

8. A big _____ fell on the city _____ and made a hole in the street.

9. I asked Sally to _____ me a(n) _____ of paper to write the note on.

10. We put our money in the _____ close to the river _____.

Name_____

Practice 8

Directions: Read each sentence carefully. Think of a word that is spelled the same but has different meanings that fits the blanks of the sentence and makes sense. Put the word in the blanks. The first is done for you.

1. I will ___cart___ the leaves away in my ___cart___ .

2. Don't _____ my milk _____ so much.

3. We did not _____ to be _____ to the _____ man, so we said that we were sorry.

4. As the train went over the _____, my brother and sister were playing _____.

5. We used _____ to _____ the broken paper box.

6. Many people bought tickets at the _____ office to watch the fighters _____.

7. The _____ of the tribe gave the _____ reason for not going to the meeting.

8. You are the _____ who is number _____ in the class.

9. The _____ was about children who _____ make-believe games.

Comprehension Strategies for an Integrated Language Arts Classroom © 1994 Fearon Teacher Aids

Practice 9

Directions: Read each set of sentences carefully. Think of a word that is spelled the same but has different meanings that fits each set of sentences. Put the word in the blank. The first is done for you.

1. You weigh yourself on these. A fish has these. ___scales___

2. You call pennies, nickels, and dimes this. You do this with your clothing. _____

3. You do this to an envelope. This animal lives in the water, and it can be trained to balance a ball on its nose. _____

4. You can lie on this in the water. You can do this in the water. _____

5. This is an insect. A plane does this. _____

6. You eat soup out of this. You play this sport with a large, hard ball. _____

7. You can write one of these. There are 26 of them in the alphabet. _____

8. You do this to get somewhere. You shovel this when it is covered with snow. _____

9. You wear this under a dress. If this happens, you may fall. _____

Name_____

Practice 10

Directions: Read each set of sentences carefully. Think of a word that is spelled the same but has different meanings that fits each set of sentences. Put the word in the blank.

1. A man usually wears this. You do this to a rope. _____

2. You wear these to help you see better. You can drink out of these. _____

3. A bell does this. You can wear it on your finger. _____

4. You need this if you are tired. It's what is left over. _____

5. This person plays baseball. It can hold water. _____

6. This can be a room. It's what you need to do to do well on a test. _____

7. This holds things. You can float on it in the water. _____

8. You need this to mail a letter. You can do this with your foot._____

9. This is a baby goat. It's a child. It's also done to fool you. _____

10. This is a bird. It's also a machine. _____

11. This is put in a lock. This is the main thing. _____

12. When you do this to your fingers, you make a noise. Clothing may have this. _____

Section Three

Fun With Words: Word Riddles and Word Puzzles

Fun with Words is a special section that your students should find challenging and enjoyable. Similar activities are grouped together and based on graduated levels of difficulty within each group. However, feel free to change the order to any sequence that will better suit the needs of your students.

The objectives for each similar group of activities state the various skills included in the groups of activities.

Learning Objectives

Activities 1-16: Word Riddles

To use reasoning ability and vocabulary skills in following directions to solve the different word riddles.

Activities 17-33: Word Puzzles

To use vocabulary skills, spelling skills, and following-direction skills to solve the various word puzzles.

Activities 34-42: Word Square Puzzles

To use visual discrimination, vocabulary skills, and spelling skills to find the required number of words or the special words in each word square puzzle.

Activities 43-52: Word Riddle Puzzles

To use visual discrimination, following-directions skills, and synthesis skills to solve each of the word riddle puzzles.

Activities 53-65: Rhyming Word Puzzles

To use auditory and/or visual discrimination and vocabulary skills to solve the rhyming word puzzles.

Activities 66-76: Scrambled Word Puzzles

To use visual discrimination, vocabulary skills, spelling skills, and synthesis skills to solve each scrambled word puzzle.

Activities 77-82: Hidden Word Puzzles

To use visual discrimination, spelling skills, vocabulary skills, and categorizing skills to solve the hidden word puzzles.

Activities 83-88: Hidden Clue Puzzles

To use visual discrimination skills, vocabulary skills, spelling skills, and categorizing skills to solve the hidden clue puzzles.

Student's Name _____

Assessment Tool Progress Report

Progress

Improvement

Comments

Word Riddles 1

Let's go on a farm-animal hunt. Below are riddles with a word following each. If you follow directions and solve the riddle, you will hunt down the animals.

1. Change one of my letters, and I'll give you milk.   cot

2. Change one of my letters, and I'll quack.   luck

3. Change one of my letters, and I'll lay an egg.   pen

4. Take away one of my letters, and I'll eat hay.   hoarse

Comprehension Strategies for an Integrated Language Arts Classroom © 1994 Fearon Teacher Aids

Word Riddles 2

Let's go on a farm-animal hunt. Below are riddles with a word following each. If you follow directions and solve the riddle, you will hunt down the animals.

1. Change one of my letters, and I'll oink.   pit

2. Change one of my letters, and I'll bark.   log

3. Change one of my letters, and I'll bray.   mile

4. Change one of my letters, and I'll go for a swim.   loose

Word Riddles 3

Let's go on a wild-animal hunt. Below are riddles with a word following each.
If you follow directions and solve the riddle, you will hunt down the animals.
Be careful. It's hard to hunt these animals down.

1. Add one letter to me, and I'll climb a tree.   money

2. Change two of my letters, and I'll run swiftly
   through the woods.   seed

3. Change two of my letters, and I'll roar.   lime

4. Change one letter, then take away one letter,
   and you'll have a striped animal.   finger

Comprehension Strategies for an Integrated Language Arts Classroom © 1994 Fearon Teacher Aids

Word Riddles 4

Let's go on a wild-animal hunt. Below are riddles with a word following each.
If you follow directions and solve the riddle, you will hunt down the animals.
Be careful. It's hard to hunt these animals down.

1. Change one letter, and you'll have a smart animal.   box

2. Change one letter, and you'll know whom
   Little Red Riding Hood met.   golf

3. Change one letter, then take away one letter,
   and you'll have an animal that likes honey.   heart

4. Change one letter, then add one letter, and you'll
   have a very dangerous animal.   father

Name_____

Word Riddles 5

See how many of the word riddles you can solve.

1. I'm the opposite of *end*. Take away one of my letters, and you will see me on a clear night. _____ _____

2. I come from the sky. Add one letter to me, and you can ride away.

   _____ _____

3. This is what you do to a book. Add one letter to me, and you'll have something to eat. _____ _____

4. This is something you like to do. Take away one of my letters, and you'll know what hens do with eggs. _____ _____

Comprehension Strategies for an Integrated Language Arts Classroom © 1994 Fearon Teacher Aids

Name_____

Word Riddles 6

See how many of the word riddles you can solve.

1. I'm something you eat out of. Take away one of my letters, and I'll fly away.
   _____ _____

2. I'm the opposite of *early*. Add one letter to me, and you can eat
   off me. _____ _____

3. I'm another word for *girl*. Add one letter to me, and you can drink
   out of me. _____ _____

4. I'm an insect that makes honey. Add three letters to me, and I'll become
   an insect that eats leaves. _____ _____

Word Riddles 7

See how many of the word riddles you can solve.

1. I grow in the ground. Take away two of my letters, and I'll crawl all over the ground. _____ _____

2. I get this when I am cold. Take away two of my letters, and you'll know what may happen to me if I get too cold. _____ _____

3. I'm used as a signal. Take away one of my letters, and I become an insect.
   _____ _____

4. I'm a female deer. Add one letter to me, and I become a bird of peace.
   _____ _____

Comprehension Strategies for an Integrated Language Arts Classroom © 1994 Fearon Teacher Aids

Name_____

Word Riddles 8

See how many of the word riddles you can solve.

1. I'm something you do in an airplane. Add one letter to me, and you'll have an important member of a wedding party._____ _____

2. I'm found in a house. Add one letter to me, and you'll have another important member of a wedding party._____ _____

3. I'm an insect. Add two letters to me, and you'll also find me at the wedding.

    _____ _____

4. I'm the opposite of *thin*. Add three letters to me, and you'll also find me at the wedding. _____ _____

Name_____

Word Riddles 9

See how many of the word riddles you can solve.

1. I help get you to school on time. Take away one of my letters, and I'll help keep anyone out of your room. _____ _____

2. Plants grow in me. Add one letter to me, and you'll know what happens to foods if they stay out too long. _____ _____

3. You do this to leaves. Add one letter to me, and you'll have something that stops a car. _____ _____

4. I'm good to eat. Add one letter to me, and you may find me in an oyster.
_____ _____

Comprehension Strategies for an Integrated Language Arts Classroom © 1994 Fearon Teacher Aids

Name_____

Word Riddles 10

See how many of the word riddles you can solve.

1. I'm something that helps you row a boat. Add two letters to me, and you can write on me. _____ _____

2. I mean the same as *steal*. Add one letter to me, and you can wear me. _____ _____

3. I'm something you take when you are sick. Take away one of my letters, and you can walk on me. _____ _____

4. I'm a cloth you throw away. Add one letter to me and I'll boast.

_____ _____

Name_____

Word Riddles 11

See how many of the word riddles you can solve.

1. I'm what you do when you study at the last moment for a test. Add one letter to me, and you'll know what you can get if you sit in the same position too long.

   _____ _____

2. I'm a person who tries to make your stay comfortable and pleasant. Add one letter to me, and I'll be able to haunt you.

   _____ _____

3. I'm a bird. Add two letters to me, and I'll become a tool that will help you untwist things. _____ _____

4. I'm found at the base of a window. Add one letter to me, and I'll become foolish. _____ _____

Comprehension Strategies for an Integrated Language Arts Classroom © 1996 Fearon Teacher Aids

Name_____

Word Riddles 12

See how many of the word riddles you can solve.

1. My first word is something that you can ride in. My second word is the opposite of *out*. Put us together, and you have a place at which you can stay.

   _____ _____ _____

2. My first word means *steal.* My second word is the opposite of *out*. Put us together, and I will fly away.

   _____ _____ _____

3. My first word is another word for friend. My second word is a high card. Put us together, and you will have a very beautiful place.

   _____ _____ _____

4. My first word is something you cook in. My second word is a three-letter word that means *attempt*. Put us together, and you have a place to store things.

   _____ _____

Name_____

Word Riddles 13

See how many of the word riddles you can solve.

1. My first word is something that you ride in. My second word weighs a lot.
    Put us together, and you have something that holds things.

    _____   _____   _____

2. My first word is part of your body. My second word is a small word that
    is used a lot. Put us together, and you have a covering that is worn in battle.

    _____   _____   _____

3. My first word is something you drink out of. My second word is something
    you can use for building. Put us together, and you have a place to store what
    I was drinking out of.

    _____   _____   _____

4. My first word is something you can sleep on. My second word weighs a lot.
    Put us together, and you have very soft material.

    _____   _____   _____

Comprehension Strategies for an Integrated Language Arts Classroom © 1994 Fearon Teacher Aids

Name _____

Word Riddles 14

Below are four sets of riddles. One word fits each set of riddles. Find the word.

Example: I'm used at the beginning of a sentence, and I'm the seat of government.
Answer: capital

1. I'm a color, and I'm good to eat. _____

2. You can do this to animals, and you can ride in me. _____

3. I'm part of a tree, and dogs do this. _____

4. I'm what you do to a car, and you can play in me. _____

Word Riddles 15

Below are four sets of riddles. One word fits each set of riddles. Find the word.

1. A plant needs me and so does a tooth. _____

2. I'm good to eat, but I can cause you lots of trouble if you get caught in me.
   _____

3. I'm something babies like to play with, but look out if I come after you.
   _____

4. I can head a country, and I can help you make straight lines. _____

Comprehension Strategies for an Integrated Language Arts Classroom © 1994 Fearon Teacher Aids

Name_____

Word Riddles 16

Below are four sets of riddles. One word fits each set of riddles. Find the word.

1. I'm a card game, and cars go over me. _____

2. Children play with me; I can be used to build houses,
   and a football player does this. _____

3. I'm a large hole, and I can be found in many fruits. _____

4. I can make music, and I can be worn around the arm or head. _____

Word Puzzles 17

Fill in the spaces to make ten four-letter words. To help you, a clue and a letter are given for each word.

1. Animals live in this building.   __ A __ __

2. Something hot can do this.   __ U __ __

3. You do this to leaves.   __ A __ __

4. You play with this.   __ A __ __

5. You ride this on the snow.   __ L __ __

6. This is the opposite of mean.   __ I __ __

7. This is another word for ill.   __ I __ __

8. This is a color.   __ L __ __

9. This is a wild animal.   __ O __ __

10. This is a bird found on a farm.   __ U __ __

Comprehension Strategies for an Integrated Language Arts Classroom © 1994 Fearon Teacher Aids

Word Puzzles 18

Below are ten clues for ten words. Each word has three letters, and the first and last letters are the same. The first is done for you.

1. A way of saying *father*.　　　　　　　　dad

2. A small child.

3. A baby wears this.

4. This is a way of saying *mother*.

5. This is a relative.

6. This is another way of saying *father*.

7. This is a person who belongs to the church.

8. This is a joke.

9. This is a young dog.

10. This is something you see with.

Name_____

Word Puzzles 19

Below are five clues for five words. The last two letters of the word that comes before begins the next word. The first is done for you.

1. This is an animal. _____cat_____

2. You did this when you were hungry. _____

3. You brush these. _____

4. You use this in sewing. _____

5. You do this to numbers. _____

Word Puzzles 20

Below are six clues for six words. The last two letters of the word that comes before begins the next word. The first is done for you.

1. This is a friend. _____pal_____

2. You are this when no one is around. _____

3. This is the opposite of *far*. _____

4. This is a school subject. _____

5. This makes things cold. _____

6. This is a penny. _____

Comprehension Strategies for an Integrated Language Arts Classroom © 1994 Fearon Teacher Aids

Name_____

Word Puzzles 21

Below are seven clues for seven words. The last letter of the word that comes before begins the next word. The first is done for you.

1. You read this.   _____book_____

2. This unlocks something.   _____

3. This is a color.   _____

4. This is what you do to keep clean.   _____

5. This is where you live.   _____

6. This is part of your head.   _____

7. This is a flower.   _____

Word Puzzles 22

Below are seven clues for seven words. The last letter of the word that comes before begins the next word.

1. This is the opposite of *princess*. _____

2. This is the opposite of *start*. _____

3. This is the opposite of *night*. _____

4. This is the opposite of *old*. _____

5. This is the opposite of *boy*. _____

6. This is the opposite of *right*. _____

7. This is the opposite of *give*. _____

Comprehension Strategies for an Integrated Language Arts Classroom ® 1994 Fearon Teacher Aids

Name_____

Word Puzzles 23

Below are four clues for four words. Each word contains a smaller word that is something to eat.

1. This is a farm animal.   _____

2. You do this if you are frightened.   _____

3. You use this to bang in a nail.   _____

4. This is a precious gem.   _____

Word Puzzles 24

Below are four clues for four words. Each word contains a smaller word that is part of your body.

1. You sit in this.   _____

2. This comes from your eyes.   _____

3. You find animals here.   _____

4. This is a nut.   _____

Word Puzzles 25

Below are four clues for four words. Each word has a smaller word in it that is a number.

1. Something sweet that bears like.   _____

2. Many times.   _____

3. Cargo.   _____

4. To be present.   _____

Name_____

Word Puzzles 26

Below are five clues for five words. Each new word uses all the letters of the word above it and also adds one letter. To make each new word, you may place the letters in any way you wish. The first is done for you.

1. This is a small word. (one letter)   _____a_____

2. This is another way of saying *mother*. (two letters)   _____

3. This is the opposite of *woman*. (three letters)   _____

4. A lion has this. (four letters)   _____

5. This is a state in the Northeast. (five letters)   _____

Word Puzzles 27

Below are five clues for five words. Each new word uses all the letters of the word above it and also adds one letter. To make each new word, you may place the letters in any way you wish. The first is done for you.

1. This is a pronoun. (one letter)   _____I_____

2. This is a greeting. (two letters)   _____

3. This is what a baseball bat does. (three letters)   _____

4. This is the opposite of *fat*. (four letters)   _____

5. You do this in your mind. (five letters)   _____

Name_____

Word Puzzles 28

Below are eight clues for eight words. Each new word has four letters. Start at number 1 and go on changing only one letter in each word to make a new word. The first is done for you.

1. You eat this.   _____food_____

2. This is the opposite of *bad*.   _____

3. This is a color.   _____

4. This is the opposite of *hot*.   _____

5. This is something that was said.   _____

6. This is something you pay to pass a bridge.   _____

7. This is made out of dough.   _____

8. This is a part you can play.   _____

Word Puzzles 29

Below are eight clues for eight words. Each word has five letters. Start at number 1 and go on changing only one letter in each word to make a new word. The first is done for you.

1. You use this to light something.   _____match_____

2. You do this to a ball.   _____

3. Chickens do this from eggs.   _____

4. You put this on a door.   _____

5. You put this on torn clothes.   _____

6. A baseball player does this.   _____

7. This woman is found in fairy tales.   _____

8. This helps you to tell the time.   _____

Comprehension Strategies for an Integrated Language Arts Classroom © 1994 Fearon Teacher Aids

Name_____

Word Puzzles 30

Below are seven clues for seven words. Each word has one more letter than the one before it. Each word also begins with the next letter of the alphabet. The first is done for you.

1. A very small word.   <u>A</u>

2. Another small word that is used a lot.   ___ ___

3. This holds things.   ___ ___ ___

4. You have this when there is no light.   ___ ___ ___ ___

5. This is the opposite of *exit*.   ___ ___ ___ ___ ___

6. This is a parent.   ___ ___ ___ ___ ___ ___

7. You throw this out.   ___ ___ ___ ___ ___ ___ ___

Word Puzzles 31

Below are seven clues for seven words. Each word is a three-letter word and the middle letter of the word starts with the next letter of the alphabet. The first is done for you.

1. I'm a high card in a deck of cards.   <u>A</u> <u>C</u> <u>E</u>

2. You do this to numbers.   ___ ___ ___

3. I'm an insect.   ___ ___ ___

4. I'm the opposite of *on*.   ___ ___ ___

5. I tell how old you are.   ___ ___ ___

6. I'm the opposite of *he*.   ___ ___ ___

7. I have a sharp point.   ___ ___ ___

Word Puzzles 32

Below are six clues for six words. Each word begins and ends with the same letter.

1. A lion does this.   _____

2. You can do this to bread.   _____

3. This is put in a lamp.   _____

4. A bell makes this sound.   _____

5. This is the opposite of *low*.   _____

6. This is the opposite of *front*.   _____

Word Puzzles 33

Below are five clues for five words. The first letter of the word is the same as the last letter of the word. The second letter of the word is the same as the next-to-last letter of the word.

Example: *sees*.
The letter *s* is the first and last letter of the word and the letter *e* is the second and next-to-last letter of the word.

1. Midday.   _____

2. To blow a horn.   _____

3. A chick says this.   _____

4. This is a person who likes books a lot.   _____

5. Something that is done.   _____

Comprehension Strategies for an Integrated Language Arts Classroom © 1994 Fearon Teacher Aids

Name _____

Word Square Puzzle 34

Below is a word square puzzle. It has ten color words in it. You can go across and down to find the words. See how many you can find.

```
A D P G R A Y
O E U R E D E
R B R O W N L
A R P I N K L
N B L U E O O
G R E E N N W
E B L A C K Y
```

1. _____   6. _____

2. _____   7. _____

3. _____   8. _____

4. _____   9. _____

5. _____   10. _____

Word Square Puzzle 35

Below is a word square puzzle. It has the name of fourteen things to eat and drink in it. You can go across and down to find the words. See how many you can find.

```
B R E A D C H
U A G P A O A
T I G P T O M
T S E L E K E
E I P E A I A
R N F I G E T
M I L K N U T
```

1. _____   8. _____

2. _____   9. _____

3. _____   10. _____

4. _____   11. _____

5. _____   12. _____

6. _____   13. _____

7. _____   14. _____

Comprehension Strategies for an Integrated Language Arts Classroom © 1994 Fearon Teacher Aids

Name_____

Word Square Puzzle 36

Below is a word square puzzle. It has fifteen animal words hidden in it. You can go across and down to find words. See how many you can find.

```
A G C A T O E
F O W L I O N
O A P I G L A
X T O H E N M
D U C K R A T
W O L F A P E
M U L E D O G
```

1. _____

2. _____

3. _____

4. _____

5. _____

6. _____

7. _____

8. _____

9. _____

10. _____

11. _____

12. _____

13. _____

14. _____

15. _____

Name_____

Word Square Puzzle 37

Below is a word square puzzle. It has twelve things to wear in it. You can go across and down to find words. See how many you can find.

```
S K I R T D S
H G C L R R H
I L S H O E O
R O L A B S R
T V I T E S T
K E P A N T S
C A P E B O W
```

1. _____   7. _____

2. _____   8. _____

3. _____   9. _____

4. _____   10. _____

5. _____   11. _____

6. _____   12. _____

Name_____

Word Square Puzzle 38

Below is a word square puzzle. It has nine words that tell you how food can taste.
You can go across and down to find words. See how many you can find.

```
O I L Y S B
G O O D A A
A O C O L D
M E H O T R
S P I C Y Y
B U R N T W
```

1. _____   5. _____

2. _____   6. _____

3. _____   7. _____

4. _____   8. _____

9. _____

Comprehension Strategies for an Integrated Language Arts Classroom © 1994 Fearon Teacher Aids

Name_____

Word Square Puzzle 39

Below is a word square puzzle. It has nine words that tell you how things can feel when you touch them. You can go across and down to find words. See how many you can find.

```
D E S O F T
A E M D R Y
M R O U G H
P C O L D A
W E T I O R
A E H O T D
```

1._____   5._____

2._____   6._____

3._____   7._____

4._____   8._____

9._____

Comprehension Strategies for an Integrated Language Arts Classroom © 1994 Fearon Teacher Aids

Name_____

Word Square Puzzle 40

Below is a Hunting Square. If you follow the directions carefully, you will track down the animal that escaped from the zoo.

```
A F A R M S
P L G O G R
S T R E E T
S T O P I T
R O C D I P
B A K E S C
```

Directions: The last word of each clue is hidden in the square. Each clue below also helps you find a letter of the animal that escaped from the zoo. Read each clue carefully and then put the letters together to hunt down the animal.

Clues:

1. Go to the end of *street*.   _____

2. Look in the center of *pit*.   _____

3. Look at what is above *rock*.   _____

4. Look at the end of *tree*.   _____

5. Look in the middle of *farms*.   _____

                    Answer: _____

Word Square Puzzle 41

Below is a word square puzzle. It has seven words that tell how you may feel when you are having fun. You can go across and down to find words. See how many you can find.

```
A M J O L L Y
L E L C C A H
B R I G H T A
G R V E E O P
L Y E Y E O P
A M L E R R Y
D E Y A Y O E
```

1. _____   4. _____

2. _____   5. _____

3. _____   6. _____

7. _____

Comprehension Strategies for an Integrated Language Arts Classroom © 1994 Fearon Teacher Aids

Word Square Puzzle 42

Below is a word square puzzle. It has twelve words that tell how you may feel when you are *not* having fun. You can go across and down to find words. See how many you can find.

```
U N H A P P Y W
N L E G M A D R
J O Y L E S S E
S W D O W N A T
O U B O R E D C
U A R M E A N H
R E A Y O U R E
U N L U C K Y D
```

1. _____   7. _____

2. _____   8. _____

3. _____   9. _____

4. _____   10. _____

5. _____   11. _____

6. _____   12. _____

Name_____

Word Riddle Puzzle 43

Below are six clues for six words. First figure out each word from the clue and write it in the space provided. When you put the first letter of each word together, you will have an animal that will have something in it to help you unlock your door.

1. I'm a female deer. _____

2. I'm a very strong animal. _____

3. I'm a sound a horse makes. _____

4. I'm an animal with a pouch. _____

5. I'm an animal that has a trunk. _____

6. I'm the day before today. _____

_ _ _ _ _ _

Comprehension Strategies for an Integrated Language Arts Classroom © 1994 Fearon Teacher Aids

Name_____

Word Riddle Puzzle 44

Below are six clues for six words. First figure out each word from the clue and write it in the space provided. When you put the first letter of each word together, you will have a very important person.

1. I'm an insect.   _____

2. I'm the opposite of *in*.   _____

3. I mean the same as *story*.   _____

4. I mean the same as *aid*.   _____

5. I'm the opposite of *begin*.   _____

6. Cars ride on me.   _____

— — — — — —

Word Riddle Puzzle 45

Below are five clues for five words. First figure out each word from the clue and write it in the space provided. When you put the first letter of each word together, you will know what has lots of keys but can't open anything.

1. I'm what you have if something hurts you.   _____

2. I'm another word for *sick*.   _____

3. I'm a relative.   _____

4. I'm part of your finger.   _____

5. I'm the opposite of *young*.   _____

— — — — —

Word Riddle Puzzle 46

Below are six clues for six words. First figure out each word from the clue and write it in the space provided. When you put the first letter of each word together, you will have the answer to this riddle: What grows smaller the longer it stays?

1. I'm what you do on a stove.   _____

2. I'm the opposite of *question*.   _____

3. I'm part of your face.   _____

4. I'm the opposite of *light*.   _____

5. I'm also part of your face.   _____

6. I'm what you do when you are hungry.   _____

—— —— —— —— —— ——

Word Riddle Puzzle 47

Each sentence below gives you a clue to a letter. Put the letters together and you will have the answer to this riddle: What howls and whistles but has no voice?

_____ 1. Its first letter is in *twist*, but not in *this*.

_____ 2. Its second letter is in *drive*, but not in *drove*.

_____ 3. Its third letter is in *twin*, but not in *twist*.

_____ 4. Its fourth letter is in *bind*, but not in *blink*.

— — — —

Word Riddle Puzzle 48

Each sentence below gives you a clue to a letter. Put the letters together and you will have the answer to this riddle: What never moves but goes up, down, and turns?

_____ 1. Its first letter is in *cart*, but not in *cat*.

_____ 2. Its second letter is in *boat,* but not in *beat*.

_____ 3. Its third letter is in *bake*, but not in *bike*.

_____ 4. Its fourth letter is in *bead*, but not in *beat*.

— — — —

Comprehension Strategies for an Integrated Language Arts Classroom © 1994 Fearon Teacher Aids

Name_____

Word Riddle Puzzle 49

Each sentence below gives you a clue to a letter. Put the letters together and you will have the answer to this riddle: What has a mouth but never eats?

_____   1. Its first letter is in *fire*, but not in *fine*.

_____   2. Its second letter is in *nine*, but not in *name*.

_____   3. Its third letter is in *live*, but not in *life*.

_____   4. Its fourth letter is in *fake*, but not in *faking*.

_____   5. Its fifth letter is in *park*, but not in *pack*.

___ ___ ___ ___ ___

Word Riddle Puzzle 50

Each sentence below gives you a clue to a letter. Put the letters together and you will have the answer to this riddle: What has lots of eyes but doesn't see?

_____   1. Its first letter is in *lap*, but not in *late*.

_____   2. Its second letter is in *boat*, but not in *beat*.

_____   3. Its third letter is in *note*, but not in *honey*.

_____   4. Its fourth letter is in *band*, but not in *bend*.

_____   5. Its fifth letter is in *feet*, but not in *fame*.

_____   6. Its sixth letter is in *grow*, but not in *grew*.

___ ___ ___ ___ ___ ___

Word Riddle Puzzle 51

Each sentence below gives you a clue to a letter. Put the letters together and you will have the answer to this riddle: What small thing never runs out of light in the night?

_____   1. Its first letter is in *fall*, but not in *tall*.

_____   2. Its second letter is in *time*, but not in *tame*.

_____   3. Its third letter is in *barn*, but not in *band*.

_____   4. Its fourth letter is in *bake*, but not in *baking*.

_____   5. Its fifth letter is in *fan*, but not in *tan*.

_____   6. Its sixth letter is in *sled*, but not in *stayed*.

_____   7. Its seventh letter is in *buy*, but not in *bus*.

___ ___ ___ ___ ___ ___ ___

Name _____

Word Riddle Puzzle 52

Each sentence below gives you a clue to a letter. Put the letters together and you will have the answer to this riddle: What has a head but does not think?

_____   1. Its first letter is in *table*, but not in *bathe*.

_____   2. Its second letter is in *fell*, but not in *fall*.

_____   3. Its third letter is in *plant*, but not in *plane*.

_____   4. Its fourth letter is in *cut*, but not in *cup*.

_____   5. Its fifth letter is in *butter*, but not in *batter*.

_____   6. Its sixth letter is in *piece*, but not in *pipes*.

_____   7. Its seventh letter is in *west*, but not in *twist*.

      __ __ __ __ __ __ __

Rhyming Word Puzzles 53

Below are some clues. Each clue will help you figure out the word it refers to. Hint: All the words rhyme.

1. This is the opposite of *fat*.   _____

2. This holds things together.   _____

3. A fish has this.   _____

4. This is part of your face.   _____

5. This is what you try to do when you play a game.   _____

6. This can hold or store things.   _____

Comprehension Strategies for an Integrated Language Arts Classroom © 1996 Fearon Teacher Aids

Rhyming Word Puzzles 54

Below are some clues. Each clue will help you figure out the word it refers to.
Hint: All the words rhyme.

1. You use this to call someone. _____

2. You make this sound when something hurts you. _____

3. This is a part of the body that you can break. _____

4. Pine trees have this. _____

5. You can get this from a bank. _____

6. This is a male bee. _____

Rhyming Word Puzzles 55

Below are some clues. Each clue will help you figure out the word it refers to.
Hint: All the words rhyme.

1. You do this to your hair.   _____

2. You live here.   _____

3. This is a large round roof.   _____

4. A car may be trimmed with this.   _____

5. This is a city in Italy.   _____

6. This is a folktale person.   _____

Comprehension Strategies for an Integrated Language Arts Classroom © 1994 Fearon Teacher Aids

Name_____

Rhyming Word Puzzles 56

Below are some clues. Each clue will help you figure out the word it refers to.
Hint: All the words rhyme.

1. You say this to quiet someone.   _____

2. You do this when you are in a hurry.   _____

3. This is partly melted snow.   _____

4. You do this when you squeeze something together. _____

5. This is a command given to a sled-drawn dog team. _____

6. You do this when your cheeks get red.   _____

Rhyming Word Puzzles 57

Below are some clues. Each clue will help you figure out the word it refers to. Hint: All the words rhyme.

1. You do this in a chair. _____

2. You want your clothes to do this. _____

3. You do this to a ball. _____

4. You use this glove in baseball. _____

5. This is a large hole. _____

6. You do this to wool. _____

7. This is a small amount of something. _____

Comprehension Strategies for an Integrated Language Arts Classroom © 1994 Fearon Teacher Aids

Name_____

Rhyming Word Puzzles 58

Below are some clues. Each clue will help you figure out the word it refers to.
Hint: All the words rhyme.

1. You use this to cool yourself.   _____

2. Your father is this.   _____

3. The sun can do this to you.   _____

4. You put things in this.   _____

5. You did this when you were in a rush.   _____

6. You cook in this.   _____

7. This is a boy's name.   _____

Rhyming Word Puzzles 59

Below are some clues. Each clue will help you figure out the word it refers to.
Hint: All the words rhyme.

1. You like to play this. _____

2. This is the opposite of *wild*. _____

3. You have this if you are well-known. _____

4. This is the opposite of *different*. _____

5. You may be this if you hurt your leg. _____

6. This comes from fire. _____

7. This tells who you are. _____

Comprehension Strategies for an Integrated Language Arts Classroom © 1994 Fearon Teacher Aids

Name_____

Rhyming Word Puzzles 60

Below are some clues. Each clue will help you figure out the word it refers to.
Hint: All the words rhyme.

1. You bounce this.   _____

2. This is part of a room.   _____

3. This is found in a house.   _____

4. This is the opposite of *short*.   _____

5. You do this when you phone.   _____

6. This is a large shopping center.   _____

7. An animal is kept in this.   _____

Rhyming Word Puzzles 61

The answers for each of the following clues are two rhyming words.

Example: amusing rabbit   Answer: funny bunny

1. wicked boy   _____ _____

2. heavy mouse chaser   _____ _____

3. high fence   _____ _____

4. comfortable insect   _____ _____

Comprehension Strategies for an Integrated Language Arts Classroom © 1994 Fearon Teacher Aids

Name_____

Rhyming Word Puzzles 62

The answers for each of the following clues are two rhyming words.

Example: dairy knife   Answer: butter cutter

1. large hog   _____ _____

2. damp animal   _____ _____

3. foolish horse   _____ _____

4. cross royal lady   _____ _____

Rhyming Word Puzzles 63

The answers for each of the following clues are two rhyming words.

Example: unhappy boy   Answer: sad lad

1. something you just bought to
   wear on your foot   _____ _____

2. little scarf   _____ _____

3. stupid friend   _____ _____

4. small boxed goodies   _____ _____

Comprehension Strategies for an Integrated Language Arts Classroom © 1994 Fearon Teacher Aids

Name_____

Rhyming Word Puzzles 64

The answers for each of the following clues are two rhyming words.

1. ill fowl   _____   _____

2. untamed young person   _____   _____

3. peculiar whiskers   _____   _____

4. boring bird   _____   _____

Rhyming Word Puzzles 65

The answers for each of the following clues are two rhyming words.

1. large music group   _____   _____

2. head robber   _____   _____

3. pleasant little animals that eat cheese   _____   _____

4. blonde locks   _____   _____

Scrambled Word Puzzles 66

Two words are put together to make a scrambled set. The letters for each word in the scrambled set are given in order, but the words are mixed together. A clue is given for each set. The first is done for you.

1. two farm animals   hceown   _hen_   _cow_

2. two house animals   dcoagt   _____   _____

3. two wild animals   faopxe   _____   _____

4. two colors   rgereden   _____   _____

5. two fruits   papeplare   _____   _____

Comprehension Strategies for an Integrated Language Arts Classroom © 1994 Fearon Teacher Aids

Name_____

Scrambled Word Puzzles 67

Two words are put together to make a scrambled set. The letters for each word in the scrambled set are given in order, but the words are mixed together. A clue is given for each set.

1. two writing things   ppaedn   _____ _____

2. two things to wear   hsoactk   _____ _____

3. two drinks   jmuiiclek   _____ _____

4. two insects   maontth   _____ _____

5. two pets   hdamostger   _____ _____

Scrambled Word Puzzles 68

Two words are put together to make a scrambled set. The letters for each word in the scrambled set are given in order, but the words are mixed together. A clue is given for each set.

1. two boys' names   msatrevke   _____ _____

2. two girls' names   csaharrooln   _____ _____

3. two dairy foods   mbiutltekr   _____ _____

4. two games   thenocnkiesy   _____ _____

5. two months   jmaurnech   _____ _____

Comprehension Strategies for an Integrated Language Arts Classroom © 1994 Fearon Teacher Aids

Name_____

Scrambled Word Puzzles 69

Here are six words—each with a clue. Change the letters of each word so that they fit the clue for a new word. The first is done for you.

1. was: You use this to cut down a tree. _____saw_____

2. raw: This is the opposite of *peace*. _____

3. tip: This is a large hole. _____

4. not: This weighs a lot. _____

5. now: The opposite of *lost*. _____

6. sag: A car needs this to run. _____

Scrambled Word Puzzles 70

Here are six words—each with a clue. Change the letters of each word so that they fit the clue for a new word. The first is done for you.

1. but: You bathe in this.   <u>   tub   </u>

2. nip: This has a point.   _____

3. gip: This is a farm animal.   _____

4. mad: This holds back water.   _____

5. pea: This is a wild animal.   _____

6. leaf: This is an insect.   _____

Comprehension Strategies for an Integrated Language Arts Classroom © 1994 Fearon Teacher Aids

Name_____

Scrambled Word Puzzles 71

Here are six words—each with a clue. Change the letters of each word so that they fit the clue for a new word. The first is done for you.

1. grin: You wear this on your finger. ___ring___

2. dear: This is something you do to a book. _____

3. life: You do this to your nails. _____

4. rare: This means *in the back*. _____

5. lame: This is a man. _____

6. late: This is a story. _____

Scrambled Word Puzzles 72

Here are six words—each with a clue. Change the letters of each word so that they fit the clue for a new word. The first is done for you.

1. hint: This is the opposite of *fat*.   _____thin_____

2. name: This is part of a horse.   _____

3. paws: This is an insect.   _____

4. deal: A pencil has this.   _____

5. fowl: This is a wild animal.   _____

6. mile: This is a fruit.   _____

Name_____

Scrambled Word Puzzles 73

Here are six words—each with a clue. Change the letters of each word so that they fit the clue for a new word.

1. mean: This tells who you are. _____

2. save: This holds flowers. _____

3. take: This is a girl's name. _____

4. sole: You don't want to do this in a game. _____

5. more: This is a city in Italy. _____

6. lamp: This is a tree. _____

Comprehension Strategies for an Integrated Language Arts Classroom © 1994 Fearon Teacher Aids

Name_____

Scrambled Word Puzzles 74

Below are sentences with a word, a letter, and a clue. Put the word and letter together and you will have the answer to the clue. You can rearrange the letters in any way. The first is done for you.

1. *No* plus *e* equals a number. _____one_____

2. *On* plus *w* equals what you did when you
   beat the other team. _____

3. *As* plus *e* equals an ocean. _____

4. *Ow* plus *t* equals a number. _____

5. *To* plus *e* equals part of your foot. _____

Comprehension Strategies for an Integrated Language Arts Classroom © 1994 Fearon Teacher Aids

Name_____

Scrambled Word Puzzles 75

Below are sentences with a word, a letter, and a clue. Put the word and letter together and you will have the answer to the clue. You can rearrange the letters in any way. The first is done for you.

1. *Dear* plus *b* equals what a man can grow
on his face.   ____beard____

2. *Beak* plus *r* equals what happens to glasses
when they fall.   _____

3. *Sow* plus *h* equals something you can watch.   _____

4. *Pie* plus *r* equals what a fruit is when it is
fully developed.   _____

5. *Salt* plus *b* equals a loud noise.   _____

Scrambled Word Puzzles 76

Below are sentences with a word, two letters, and a clue. Put the word and letters together and you will have the answer to the clue. You can rearrange the letters in any way.

1. *Ear* plus *m* and *d* equals what you do
   when you sleep.   _____

2. *Hear* plus *c* and *s* equals what you do when
   you look for someone or something.   _____

3. *Bale* plus *c* and *h* equals something that
   gets clothes white.   _____

4. *Soar* plus *b* and *b* equals what a towel does.   _____

Comprehension Strategies for an Integrated Language Arts Classroom © 1994 Fearon Teacher Aids

Hidden Word Puzzles 77

Find the word that is hidden in each sentence. The words following the sentence will tell you what to look for. Hint: The answer may be hidden in one or more words of the sentence. The first is done for you.

1. I spent some time at the fair. (something you write with)

   s*pen*t—pen

2. I have a pretty dresser in my room. (something a girl wears)

   _____

3. I put my clothing in my drawer. (something that is fun to do)

   _____

4. I drink a lot of milk. (something that a pen needs)   _____

Hidden Word Puzzles 78

Find the word that is hidden in each sentence. The words following the sentence will tell you what to look for. Hint: The answer may be hidden in one or more words of the sentence. The first is done for you.

1. I play on the baseball team. (a drink)   _team—tea_

2. I can dye my dress blue. (something sweet)   _____

3. The goats butt Eric in the back. (a dairy food)   _____

4. I have finished three problems so far.
   (something to sit on)   _____

Hidden Word Puzzles 79

Find the word that is hidden in each sentence. The words following the sentence will tell you what to look for. Hint: The answer may be hidden in one or more words of the sentence.

1. I like to wear pants. (an insect)   _____

2. When are we going to the party? (a farm animal)   _____

3. I was pleased to see her. (an insect)   _____

4. I do very well in school. (a bird)   _____

Comprehension Strategies for an Integrated Language Arts Classroom © 1994 Fearon Teacher Aids

Name_____

Hidden Word Puzzles 80

Find the word that is hidden in each sentence. The words following the sentence
will tell you what to look for. Hint: The answer may be hidden in one or more words
of the sentence.

1. My mother is coming to school today. (an insect)   _____

2. I like to wear a cape. (a wild animal)   _____

3. The bird's plumes are colorful. (a fruit)   _____

4. Please eat your broth, Ernest. (a relative)   _____

Hidden Word Puzzles 81

Find the name of the vegetable that is hidden in each sentence.
Hint: The answer may be hidden in one or more words of the sentence.

1. Mary will speak to the class.   _____

2. The beetles were eating our leaves.   _____

3. She will be an animal in the play.   _____

4. The sun made our car rot.   _____

Name_____

Hidden Word Puzzles 82

Find the name of the school subject that is hidden in each sentence.
Hint: The answer may be hidden in one or more words of the sentence.

1. I will read in George's house.   _____

2. The mat had some dirt on it.   _____

3. Please give this to Ryan.   _____

4. In the story, the germ and the medicine
   fought a battle.   _____

5. The cartoon made us laugh a lot.   _____

Hidden Clue Puzzles 83

Below are six clues for six words. Each word cannot lose because it has *win* in it. The first is done for you.

1. This win is a season.   winter

2. This win is part of a bird.   _____

3. This win is something you can look through.   _____

4. This win is something you can do with your eyes.   _____

5. This win is something older people may drink.   _____

6. This win can make a breeze.   _____

Hidden Clue Puzzles 84

Below are six clues for six words. Each word weighs a lot because it has a *ton* in it.

1. A sweater may have these.   _____

2. This holds things.   _____

3. The name of the first President.   _____

4. You have this in your throat.   _____

5. You have this in your mouth.   _____

6. This is very soft.   _____

Comprehension Strategies for an Integrated Language Arts Classroom © 1994 Fearon Teacher Aids

Name _____

Hidden Clue Puzzles 85

Below are eight clues for eight words. Each word can take you for a ride because it has a *car* in it.

1. This car is a vegetable. _____

2. This car will take a baby for a ride. _____

3. This car is a four-letter word that holds things. _____

4. This car is something that you can write on. _____

5. This car is the opposite of neglect. _____

6. This car is what you need to get on a bus or taxi. _____

7. This car is something you can walk on. _____

8. This car is a girl's name. _____

Hidden Clue Puzzles 86

Below are ten clues for ten words. Each word has an *ant* in it.

1. You wear these. _____

2. This grows in the ground. _____

3. You do this to your paper when you
   write in cursive. _____

4. This is an animal with horns. _____

5. This lights up the night. _____

6. This is a very dangerous animal. _____

7. You do this when you breathe quickly. _____

8. A deer has these. _____

9. This is a former President's name. _____

10. Your television set needs this to help you
    see good pictures. _____

Comprehension Strategies for an Integrated Language Arts Classroom © 1994 Fearon Teacher Aids

Name_____

Hidden Clue Puzzles 87

Below are ten clues for ten words. Each word must have a beginning because it has an *end* in it.

1. You do this when you bow.   _____

2. You do this when you sew something that is torn.   _____

3. You may have done this when someone needed
   something that you had.   _____

4. A car has this.   _____

5. You do this when you take care of someone.   _____

6. You do this when you mix things together.   _____

7. Something soft would be this.   _____

8. A pal is this.   _____

9. A monster is also this.   _____

10. You do this when you praise someone.   _____

Hidden Clue Puzzles 88

Below are five clues for five animals. After you figure out each animal, you will be able to solve the puzzle.

1. I'm very large and heavy and carry all my things with me.
   What am I and how do I carry my things?

   _____   _____

2. I live in the water and I like to weigh myself a lot.
   What am I and why do I like to weigh myself a lot?

   _____   _____

3. I'm a rather large rodent who sews a lot.
   What am I and why do I sew a lot?

   _____   _____

4. I'm a very proud bird and I keep myself looking good all the time.
   What am I and why do I keep myself looking fine all the time?

   _____   _____

5. I'm large and can hop very fast. I take my baby with me wherever I go.
   What am I and why do I take my baby with me?

   _____   _____

Answers

Answers to Strategy 1

Practice 1 (p. 26)

1. Zip
2. Zap
3. on the moon
4. play
5. cats and rats

Practice 2 (p. 27)

1. all the cats and rats
2. a very large house
3. special air masks
4. air
5. laugh

Practice 3 (p. 28)

1. happy
2. as soon as daylight came
3. their Earth cousins
4. on the space shuttle
5. no

Practice 4 (p. 29)

1. to the library
2. to take out some books on the planet Earth and see pictures of the Earth
3. a brightly lit, round room
4. in the middle of the large house
5. books about the Earth
6. went to the letter *E*, found the word *Earth*, pressed a button
7. pictures of the Earth

Practice 5 (p. 30)

1. special clothing and air masks
2. on the space shuttle
3. their Earth cousins
4. funny
5. air masks
6. air masks
7. put on special Earth clothing
8. laugh

Answers to Strategy 2

Practice 1 (p. 37)

1. No. It is stated that they are using the same water that the first cats and rats brought with them. They came from some other place that had water.

2. There is no water on the moon and water is needed to live.

3. Air and water are precious on the moon because the moon doesn't have any. Air and water are necessary to live.

4. Air and water.

Practice 2 (p. 38)

1. No. Zip and Zap wear their space clothes and air masks in the spaceship.

2. No. It is stated that the spaceship is the same one that brought Zip and Zap to the moon.

3. Yes. It is their means of travel. It is stated that there are special cats and rats who take care of the spaceship and that the spaceship is well taken care of.

4. Yes. Every month the school goes on a space trip.

Practice 3 (p. 39)

1. Zap was wearing the special outdoor clothing because he didn't float away when he jumped up. When Zip jumped up, he floated away.

2. He wasn't wearing the special clothing.

3. He floated away because he wasn't wearing special clothing.

4. No, because he forgot to put on his special outdoor clothing.

Practice 4 (p. 40)

Answers will vary. Listed are possible answers.

1. It's kind. (It saved Zip.)

2. It knows where Zip lives. (It brings Zip to his house.)

3. It knows why Zip floated away. (It calls Zip a "suitless wonder.")

4. It seems jolly and has a sense of humor. (It says, "Ho, ho, ho." It also calls Zip a "suitless wonder.")

5. It must be large. (It was able to grab Zip, who was floating high into space. Zip heard a booming voice, but Zip didn't see where it was coming from.)

Practice 5 (p. 41)

1. true
2. true
3. can't tell
4. true
5. false
6. can't tell
7. can't tell
8. can't tell
9. true
10. can't tell

Practice 6 (p. 42)

1. can't tell
2. true
3. true
4. true
5. false

Practice 7 (p. 43)

1. true
2. false
3. can't tell
4. can't tell
5. can't tell
6. can't tell
7. true
8. true
9. can't tell
10. can't tell

Practice 8 (p. 44)

1. true
2. true
3. true
4. true
5. can't tell
6. can't tell
7. false
8. can't tell
9. can't tell
10. true

Practice 9 (p. 45)

1. false
2. true
3. false
4. true
5. can't tell
6. can't tell
7. true
8. can't tell

Practice 10 (p. 46)

Answers will vary.

1. They were lazy because they didn't bother to move the box out of the middle of the road.

   or

   They were not concerned that someone might trip over the box.

2. He didn't want to be seen and he wanted to see what the people would do when they saw the box.

3. The boy works hard. He is not lazy. He cares about other people. It said in the story that he moved the box away so that no one would trip on it.

4. Under the box.

5. The rich man.

6. The rich man wanted to find someone who wasn't lazy or was kind and reward that person. The person who went to the trouble of moving the box would find the gold.

Answers to Strategy 3

Practice 1 (p. 52)

1. Today is a special day on the moon (effect); it is Children's Day (cause)

2. Zip and Zap love this day (effect); there are lots of parties (cause)

3. The parties are fun (effect); the children play lots of games (cause)

4. The children laugh (effect); funny clowns do lots of tricks (cause)

Practice 2 (p. 53)

1. Zip and Zap ate too much (cause); they got stomachaches (effect)

2. The next day they both had to stay home (effect); they did not feel well (cause)

3. They did not want to look at food (effect); it made them sick (cause)

4. Zip and Zap went to see the doctor (effect); their stomachs hurt so much (cause)

Practice 3 (p. 54)

1. Naomi and Phil didn't play outside for two days (effect); their dads said it was too cold (cause)

2. Phil has lots of games (cause); I want to visit him (effect)

3. It was no fun (effect); when it was too cold to play outside (cause)

Practice 4 (p. 55)

1. Karesha was bored (effect); she didn't have anything to do (cause)

2. Then she asked her mother what she could do (effect); she couldn't think of anything (cause)

3. Your brother knows you love to read (cause); he brought you lots of new books from the library (effect)

4. I like this one (effect); it is so funny (cause)

Practice 5 (p. 56)

1. Linda went with her family to Seattle (effect); she wanted to visit her cousins (cause)

2. I like school (effect); there are lots of things to do (cause)

3. I like to learn about things (cause); I like school (effect)

4. The children were all happy (effect); Burt and Linda came back to school (cause)

5. Burt and Linda are a lot of fun (cause); the other children missed them (effect)

Answers to Strategy 4

Answers will vary.

Practice 1 (p. 62)

Main idea:
Zip and Zap's birthdays are fun. (4)

Sample title:
Zip and Zap's Birthday

Practice 2 (p. 63)

Main idea:
Zip and Zap's first fight makes them feel sad. (3)

Sample title:
Zip and Zap's First Fight

Practice 3 (p. 64)

Main idea: The moon's weather forces Zip and Zap to stay in their house. (5)

Sample title:
The Moon's Weather

Practice 4 (p. 65)

Main idea:
A new family becomes part of Beth's neighborhood

Sample title: The New Family in Beth's Neighborhood

Practice 5 (p. 66)

Main idea:
Fiona decides to go to a birthday party after thinking about what new friends she might make.

Sample title:
Fiona and the Birthday Party

Answers to Strategy 5

Answers will vary.

Practice 1 (p. 72)

Central idea:
Thinking of something different to do is different and hard work for Zip and Zap.

Sample title:
Zip and Zap Do Something Different

Practice 2 (p. 73)

Central idea: Zip and Zap's new moon bicycles are fun to ride.

Sample title: Zip and Zap's New Moon Bicycles

Practice 3 (p. 74)

Central idea: A rich man's plan for quiet is blocked by two carpenters.

Sample title: The Rich Man and the Carpenters

Practice 4 (p. 75)

Central idea: A clever fox outsmarts a cruel lion.

Sample title: The Clever Fox and the Cruel Lion *or* A Fox Outsmarts a Lion

Practice 5 (p. 76)

Central idea: A sad princess can't eat until she has a friend her own age to play with.

Sample title: The Sad Princess *or* The Princess Who Became Thinner and Thinner

Answers to Strategy 6

Answers to Practices 1- 5 may vary.

Answers to Strategy 7

For the student practices in this section, have students reread instructions to check their answers.

Practice 1 (p. 92)

Practice 2 (p. 93)

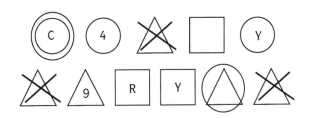

Practice 3 (p. 94)

Practice 4 (p. 95)

1.

2

3.

4.

5. 1, 3, 5, 7; 4, 6, 8, 10; O, P, Q, R

6.

Practice 5 (p. 96)

The directions state that you should read the entire list of directions carefully *before doing anything*. You should have done only numbers 6 and 7.

Practice 6 (p. 97)

1. Do nothing. There aren't three triangles.

2. Put the letter *O* in the third circle.

3. Put the number *11* in the first square.

4. Put a circle around all the circles.

Practice 7 (p. 98)

L M N O P Q 7 6 5 4 20 9

1. Do nothing. There aren't more letters than numbers.

2. Put a circle around the second triangle. The numbers 5 + 4 = 9.

3. Put the first letter *L* in the square after the third triangle.

4. Put the number 7 in the third square. There are three odd numbers and three even numbers and 6 + 5 = 11.

Practice 8 (p. 99)

1. (cat) L M N O P 7 6 5 4 man

2. b~~oy~~ in E (F) G out (fat) pan
   X

3. ☐ ☐ △ ◯

4. ◯ ◯ ◯ ◯

5. △ △ ☐ ☐

1. Put a circle around *cat* and *fat*.

2. Put an "X" on *boy*.

3. Put a circle around the letter *F*.

4. Put an "X" above the triangle in the third row.

Practice 9 (p. 100)

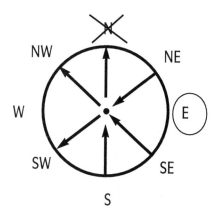

W

NW   NE

E

SW   SE

S

1. Do nothing. There is no arrow pointing *S*, *SE*, *E*, *NE*, and *W*.

2. Do nothing. There is no arrow pointing *S*.

3. Put an "X" on *N*.

4. Put a circle around *E*.

Practice 10 (p. 101)

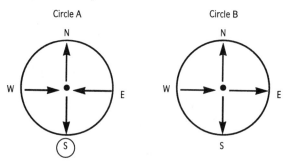

Circle A   Circle B

1. Do nothing. There is no arrow pointing *W* in Circle B.

2. Do nothing. The arrows in Circle B are not pointing in four different directions.

3. Put a circle around *S* in Circle A.

4. Do nothing. There is no arrow pointing *W* in Circle B.

Answers to Strategy 8

Practice 1 (p. 106)

Children should arrange all vegetables together, all fruits together, and all drinks together. These can be arranged according to pictures or words.

Practice 2 (p. 107)

Children should arrange the animals according to various groups—pets, farm animals, or wild animals. These can be arranged according to pictures or words.

Practice 3 (p. 108)

Children should put the household pictures under the proper headings that have been supplied.

Practice 4 (p. 109)

Children should arrange the shapes into a number of groups. The groups could be as follows: all triangles, all squares, all circles, or all small figures, all medium figures, or all large figures, for example. Some children may be divergent and come up with different kinds of groups.
For example: a triangle, square, and a circle; a large square, a medium triangle, a small circle; and so on. These children should be encouraged because the instructions were to group the shapes in as many ways as they can.

Practice 5 (p. 110)

The same as for Practice 4 except that the groups could be as follows: all hearts, all diamonds, all spades, all clubs; all 2's, all 3's, all 4's, all 5's, all 6's, and so on. The children can be divergent and come up with various different kinds of groups.

Practice 6 (p. 111)

Children can arrange the words into a number of different groups. Here are some:

Wild animals: elephant, ape, tiger
Tame animals: all the others
Fowl: hen, drake, gander, goose, turkey, duck
Female animals: hen, sow, mare
Male animals: drake, colt, gander
Pets: colt, mare, puppy, kitten, dog (Many of the other animals can be pets)
Baby animals: puppy, kitten, colt
Farm animals: hen, drake, sow, mare, colt, gander, and so on, except for the elephant, ape, and tiger
Animals: All would be included

Practice 7 (p. 112)

Children can arrange the words into a number of different groups. Here are some:

Things you find in school: Everything would be included

School persons: teacher, principal, nurse, student

Schoolbooks: history books, science books, spelling books

Things for writing: pencil, paper, desk, chalkboard, pen, chalk

Rooms in school: classroom, library, auditorium

Games and game equipment: monopoly, baseball, jump rope, basketball, chess, checkers

Indoor games: monopoly, chess, checkers

Outdoor games: baseball, jump rope, basketball

What you find in a classroom: Everything would be included except principal, library, auditorium, nurse

Children may come up with other categories

Practice 8 (p. 113)

Children can arrange the words into a number of different groups.

Things to wear: Everything would be included

Jewelry: bracelet, earrings, watch

Cold weather clothing: scarf, gloves, sweater, tights, mittens, boots, coat, socks, cap, hat

Girl clothing: dress, stockings, jeans, gown, blouse, skirt, slip, tights, pants (Girls also wear vests and shirts. These, as well as items such as socks, should also be accepted.)

Boy clothing: shirt, vest, jeans, pants. (Items such as socks and caps should also be accepted.)

Footwear: socks, shoes, boots, stockings, tights, slippers

Hand clothing: gloves, mittens

Headwear: cap, hat

Children may come up with other categories

Practice 9 (p. 114)

1. milk
2. green
3. coat
4. cat
5. circle
6. ten
7. checkers
8. Terry

Practice 10 (p. 115)

1. raisins
2. brown
3. football
4. checkers
5. gloves
6. bathing suit
7. spinach
8. ring

Practice 11 (p. 116)

1. Frank
2. spinach
3. purple
4. door
5. crayon
6. wood
7. ant
8. Susan
9. circle
10. goose

Practice 12 (p. 117)

1. banana
2. twenty
3. seven
4. sixteen
5. princess
6. doe
7. dishwasher
8. eight
9. mustard
10. chalkboard

Practice 13 (p. 118)

1. large
2. pretty
3. pleasant
4. cruel
5. leaf
6. reading
7. cat

Practice 14 (p. 119)

1. vegetables
2. shapes
3. fowl
4. nuts
5. clothing
6. colors
7. names
8. fruits
9. flowers
10. meat

Practice 15 (p. 120)

1. girls' names
2. boys' names
3. bedroom things
4. eating things
5. dried fruit
6. writing things
7. tools
8. food

Practice 16 (p. 120)

1. night
2. July
3. lime
4. fairy tales
5. airplane
6. car
7. twenty-eight (not a multiple of five)
8. United States
9. bull
10. whale (a mammal)

Practice 17 (p. 122)

1. blue
2. pig
3. ice hockey (played on ice)
4. piano
5. two
6. hair (part of the head)
7. hen
8. Europe
9. raisin
10. hoof

Practice 18 (p. 123)

1. duck
2. China
3. right
4. ape
5. mare
6. meat
7. teacher
8. bag
9. beef
10. hat (worn on head rather than body)

Practice 19 (p. 124)

1. seven
2. doe
3. mule
4. tree
5. sugar
6. sock
7. silo
8. pliers (doesn't have a sharp blade)
9. chair
10. fox

Practice 20 (p. 125)

1. Africa
2. eagle
3. long
4. silent
5. mare
6. cabin
7. bell
8. drawer
9. scarf
10. frogs (not a reptile)

Answers to Strategy 9

Practice 1 (p. 132)

Example: puppy

1. sad face
2. boy
3. bacon strips
4. queen
5. gasoline pump

Practice 2 (p. 133)

Example: sun

1. thermometer
2. fawn
3. ear
4. branch
5. raincoat

Practice 3 (p. 134)

Example: boat

1. earring
2. money
3. thumb
4. dollar
5. prunes

Practice 4 (p. 135)

Example: hat

1. two wheels
2. plane
3. leaf
4. dollar
5. hay

Practice 5 (p. 136)

Example: girl

1. red light
2. branch
3. triangle
4. trunk
5. rain

Practice 6 (p. 137)

Example: carrot

1. ears
2. hands
3. lemon
4. bulb
5. barrel

Practice 7 (p. 138)

Example: dollar

1. plane
2. quack
3. finger
4. yellow
5. write

Practice 8 (p. 139)

Example: egg

1. whoo
2. church
3. tame
4. hundred
5. dig

Practice 9 (p. 140)

1. bed
2. smell
3. wolf
4. knee
5. sentence
6. story

Practice 10 (p. 141)

1. stable
2. hot
3. drake
4. sow
5. drink
6. cruel

Practice 11 (p. 142)

1. young
2. bean
3. soft
4. cub
5. doe
6. quiet
7. always
8. weak
9. less
10. yesterday

Practice 12 (p. 143)

1. low	2. toe
3. nephew	4. neigh
5. drake	6. dollar
7. buy	8. empty
9. eat	10. wheel

Practice 13 (p. 144)

1. cold	2. even
3. dumb	4. lemon
5. vehicle	6. dollar
7. star	8. clothing
9. silk	10. eight

Practice 14 (p. 145)

1. hangar	2. sister
3. Africa	4. four
5. rough	6. drink
7. excuse	8. shout
9. turtle	10. mildew

Practice 15 (p. 146)

1. clean	2. four
3. Asia	4. country
5. Reverend	6. before
7. feet	8. gun
9. pupil	10. today

Answers to Strategy 10

Practice 1 (p. 151)

1. dry—slippery
2. scales—feathers
3. noon— night
4. bead—bread
5. sets—rises

Practice 2 (p. 152)

1. northern—western
2. dawn—dusk
3. crow— cow
4. dimes—quarters
5. bear—beard

Practice 3 (p. 153)

1. tame—wild
2. ducklings—chicks
3. mare— doe
4. salt—sugar
5. thee—three

Practice 4 (p. 154)

1. jungle—farm
2. evening—morning
3. hen— rooster
4. blowing—crowing
5. rooster—hen
6. in—on
7. three—five
8. quiet—noisy

Practice 5 (p. 155)

1. his—her
2. cloudy—sunny
3. moon—sun
4. morning—noon
5. Few—Many
6. low—loud
7. walked—stopped
8. four—three
9. Mr.— Mrs.
10. started—stopped
11. mean—kind

Answers to Strategy 11

Practice 1 (p. 160)

1. O   2. O   3. O   4. F   5. F

Practice 2 (p. 161)

1. O   2. F   3. F   4. O   5. O

Practice 3 (p. 162)

1. F   2. O   3. O   4. F   5. F

Practice 4 (p. 163)

1. O   2. O   3. F   4. O   5. F

Practice 5 (p. 164)

1. F   2. O   3. F   4. O   5. O

Answers to Strategy 12

Practice 1 (p. 173)

1. play   2. box
3. rose   4. suit
5. point

Practice 2 (p. 174)

1. pitch   2. run
3. strike   4. rest
5. bear

Practice 3 (p. 175)

1. plant   2. plum
3. monkey   4. lamb
5. iron

Practice 4 (p. 176)

1. break   2. broke
3. flowed   4. pinch
5. fast

Practice 5 (p. 177)

1. sad   2. silly
3. sick   4. good
5. tired

Practice 6 (p. 178)

1. angry   2. proud
3. insulted   4. ashamed
5. happy

Practice 7 (p. 179)

1. embarrassed 2. scared
3. joyful   4. guilty
5. peculiar

Practice 8 (p. 180)

1. hard   2. not believable
3. double   4. cure
5. rough

Practice 9 (p. 181)

1. gentle   2. well-known
3. large, huge   4. wide
5. wild, savage   6. large, big
7. brave,   8. powerful,
   courageous   strong
9. destroyed   10. equal

Practice 10 (p. 182)

Sample answers:

1. play	2. boat
3. hen	4. week
5. friend	6. zoo
7 did	8. swim
9. fruit	10. park

Practice 11 (p. 183)

Sample answers:

1. Jack	2. walk
3. school	4. baseball
5. swimming	6. do
7. Carol	8. cat
9. circus	10. dog

Practice 12 (p. 184)

1. mouse	2. in
3. is	4. smart
5. it	6. give
7. cheese	8. play
9. hide	10. seek
11. the	12. house

Practice 13 (p. 185)

1. was	2. tree
3. cat	4. branch
5. sat	6. sat
7. sat	8. to
9. down	10. meow
11. tree	12. night
13. morning	14. she
15. not	16. what
17. we	18. loud
19. my	20. ran

Practice 14 (p. 186)

1. shy	2. am
3. No	4. me
5. what	6. say
7. school	8. hand
9. never	10. peak
11. not	12. be
13. very	14. have
15. friends	

Practice 15 (p.187)

1. cookie	2. little
3. had	4. big
5. tail	6. girl
7. as	8. was
9. bunny	10. say
11. not	12. eat
13. do	14. me
15. girl	16. no
17. Look	18. at
19. looked	20. cookie
21. talking	22. eat
23. the	24. table
25. hopped	26. ran
27. but	28. catch
29. bunny	30. fast

Answers to Strategy 13

Practice 1 (p. 192)

1. big
2. ill
3. joyful
4. bright
5. handsome

Practice 2 (p. 193)

1. little
2. correct
3. mean
4. lady
5. thin

Practice 3 (p. 194)

1. price
2. pal
3. rip
4. struck
5. place

Practice 4 (p. 195)

1. wealthy
2. stupid
3. moist
4. healthy
5. finish

Practice 5 (p. 196)

1. clever
2. start
3. chum
4. head
5. aid
6. end
7. defend
8. scent
9. damage
10. trouble

Practice 6 (p. 197)

1. tall
2. little
3. low
4. later
5. back

Practice 7 (p. 198)

1. well
2. good
3. clean
4. beautiful
5. asleep

Practice 8 (p. 199)

1. sad
2. empty
3. old
4. stale
5. guilty

Practice 9 (p. 200)

1. tall, short
2. rough, soft
3. win, lose
4. rises, sets
5. wet, dry

Practice 10 (p. 201)

1. You may <u>laugh</u> when you are <u>happy</u>, and you may <u>cry</u> when you are <u>sad</u>.

2. You are usually <u>awake</u> during the <u>day</u>, and you are usually <u>asleep</u> during the <u>night</u>.

3. You are <u>strong</u> when you are <u>healthy</u>, and you are <u>weak</u> when you are <u>sick</u>.

4. When you are <u>kind</u>, people <u>love</u> you, but when you are <u>cruel</u>, people <u>hate</u> you.

5. My <u>sister</u> is <u>always</u> late, but my <u>brother</u> is <u>never</u> late.

Answers to Strategy 14

Practice 1 (p. 207)

1. can
2. bark
3. train
4. fall
5. pet

Practice 2 (p. 208)

1. swing
2. spring
3. well
4. plant
5. fan

Practice 3 (p. 209)

1. pass
2. groom
3. park
4. grade
5. fair

Practice 4 (p. 210)

1. show
2. fine
3. spell
4. hit
5. band

Practice 5 (p. 211)

1. rose
2. hose
3. point
4. jack
5. run

Practice 6 (p. 212)

1. present
2. duck
3. pin
4. coat
5. mine

Practice 7 (p. 213)

1. sun
2. ruler
3. flag
4. ball
5. shrimp
6. line
7. top
8. block
9. slip
10. bank

Practice 8 (p. 214)

1. cart
2. shake
3. mean
4. bridge
5. tape
6. box
7. chief
8. one
9. play

Practice 9 (p. 215)

1. scales
2. change
3. seal
4. float
5. fly
6. bowl
7. letter
8. walk
9. slip

Practice 10 (p. 216)

1. tie
2. glasses
3. ring
4. rest
5. pitcher
6. study
7. tube
8. stamp
9. kid
10. crane
11. key
12. snap

Answers to Fun with Words

Word Riddles 1 (p. 220)

1. cow
2. duck
3. hen
4. horse

Word Riddles 2 (p. 221)

1. pig
2. dog
3. mule
4. goose

Word Riddles 3 (p. 222)

1. monkey
2. deer
3. lion
4. tiger

Word Riddles 4 (p. 223)

1. fox
2. wolf
3. bear
4. panther

Word Riddles 5 (p. 224)

1. start—star
2. rain—train
3. read—bread
4. play—lay

Word Riddles 6 (p. 225)

1. bowl—owl
2. late—plate
3. lass—glass
4. bee—beetle

Word Riddles 7 (p. 226)

1. plant—ant
2. chill—ill
3. beep—bee
4. doe—dove

Word Riddles 8 (p. 227)

1. ride—bride
2. room—groom
3. moth— mother
4. fat—father

Word Riddles 9 (p. 228)

1. clock—lock
2. soil—spoil
3. rake—brake
4. pear—pearl

Word Riddles 10 (p. 229)

1. oar—board
2 . rob—robe
3. drug—rug
4. rag—brag

Word Riddles 11 (p. 230)

1. cram—cramp
2. host—ghost
3. wren—wrench
4. sill—silly

Word Riddles 12 (p. 231)

1. cab—in—cabin
2. rob—in—robin
3. pal—ace—palace
4. pan—try—pantry

Word Riddles 13 (p. 232)

1. car—ton—carton
2. arm—or—armor
3. cup—board—cupboard
4. cot—ton—cotton

Word Riddles 14 (p. 233)

1. orange
2. train
3. bark
4. park

Word Riddles 15 (p. 234)

1. root
2. jam
3. rattler
4. ruler

Word Riddles 16 (p. 235)

1. bridge
2. blocks
3. pit
4. band

Word Puzzles 17 (p. 236)

1. barn
2. burn
3. rake
4. game
5. sled
6. nice, kind
7. sick
8. blue
9. wolf
10. duck

Word Puzzles 18 (p. 237)

1. dad	2. tot
3. bib	4. mom
5. sis	6. pop
7. nun	8. gag
9. pup	10. eye

Word Puzzles 19 (p. 238)

1. cat	2. ate
3. teeth	4. thread
5. add	

Word Puzzles 20 (p. 238)

1. pal	2. alone
3. near	4. arithmetic
5. ice	6. cent

Word Puzzles 21 (p. 239)

1. book	2. key
3. yellow	4. wash
5. house	6. ear
7. rose	

Word Puzzles 22 (p. 240)

1. prince	2. end
3. day	4. young
5. girl	6. left
7. take	

Word Puzzles 23 (p. 241)

1. goat (oat)	2. scream (cream)
3. hammer (ham)	4. pearl (pea, pear)

Word Puzzles 24 (p. 241)

1. chair (hair)	2. tear (ear)
3. farm (arm)	4. chestnut (chest)

Word Puzzles 25 (p. 241)

1. honey (one)	2. often (ten)
3. freight (eight)	4. attend (ten)

Word Puzzles 26 (p. 242)

1. a	2. ma
3. man	4. mane
5. Maine	

Word Puzzles 27 (p.242)

1. I	2. hi
3. hit	4. thin
5. think	

Word Puzzles 28 (p. 243)

1. food	2. good
3. gold	4. cold
5. told	6. toll
7. roll	8. role

Word Puzzles 29 (p. 244)

1. match	2. catch
3. hatch	4. latch
5. patch	6. pitch
7. witch	8. watch

Word Puzzles 30 (p. 245)

1. a	2. be
3. cup, can	4. dark
5. enter	6. father
7. garbage	

Word Puzzles 31 (p. 245)

1. ace	2. add
3. bee	4. off
5. age	6. she
7. pin	

Word Puzzles 32 (p. 246)

1. roar	2. toast
3. bulb	4. gong
5. high	6. rear

Word Puzzles 33 (p. 246)

1. noon	2. toot
3. peep	4. reader
5. deed	

Word Square Puzzle 34 (p. 247)

Across: gray, red, brown, pink, blue, green, black

Down: orange, purple, yellow

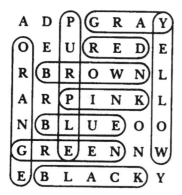

Word Square Puzzle 35 (p. 248)

Across: bread, pea, fig, milk, nut

Down: butter, raisin, egg, apple, date, tea, cookie, ham, meat

Word Square Puzzle 36 (p. 249)

Across: cat, fowl, owl, lion, pig, hen, duck, rat, wolf, ape, mule, dog

Down: fox, goat, tiger

Word Square Puzzle 37 (p. 250)

Across: skirt, shoe, pants, cape, bow

Down: shirt, glove, slip, hat, robe, dress, shorts

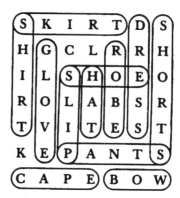

Word Square Puzzle 38 (p. 251)

Across: oily, good, cold, hot, spicy, burnt

Down: salty, bad, dry

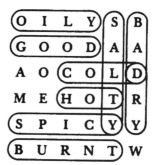

Word Square Puzzle 39 (p. 252)

Across: soft, dry, rough, cold, wet, hot

Down: damp, smooth, hard

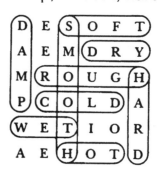

Word Square Puzzle 40 (p. 253)

1. T   2. I   3. G   4. E   5. R
Answer: TIGER

```
A  F  A (R) M  S
P  L (G) O  G  R
S  T  R  E (E)(T)
S  T  O  P (I) T
R  O  C  D  I  P
B  A  K  E  S  C
```

Word Square Puzzle 41 (p. 254)

Across: jolly, bright

Down: glad, merry, lively, cheery, happy

```
A  M  J  O  L  L  Y
L  E  L  C  C  A  H
B  R  I  G  H  T  A
G  R  V  E  E  O  P
L  Y  E  Y  E  O  P
A  M  L  E  R  R  Y
D  E  Y  A  Y  O  E
```

Word Square Puzzle 42 (p. 255)

Across: unhappy, mad, joyless, down, bored, mean, unlucky

Down: sour, low, gloomy, sad, wretched

```
U  N  H  A  P  P  Y  W
N  L  E  G  M  A  D  R
J  O  Y  L  E  S  S  E
S  W  D  O  W  N  A  T
O  U  B  O  R  E  D  C
U  A  R  M  E  A  N  H
R  E  A  Y  O  U  R  E
U  N  L  U  C  K  Y  D
```

Word Riddle Puzzle 43 (p. 256)

1. doe   2. ox
3. neigh   4. kangaroo
5. elephant   6. yesterday

Answer: DON<u>KEY</u>

Word Riddle Puzzle 44 (p. 257)

1. moth   2. out
3. tale   4. help
5. end   6. road

Answer: MOTHER

Word Riddle Puzzle 45 (p. 258)

1. pain   2. ill
3. aunt   4. nail
5. old

Answer: PIANO

Word Riddle Puzzle 46 (p. 259)

1. cook   2. answer
3. nose   4. dark
5. lip   6. eat

Answer: CANDLE

Word Riddle Puzzle 47 (p. 260)

1. W   2. I
3. N   4. D

Answer: WIND

Word Riddle Puzzle 48 (p. 260)

1. R   2. O
3. A   4. D

Answer: ROAD

Word Riddle Puzzle 49 (p. 261)

1. R   2. I
3. V   4. E
5. R

Answer: RIVER

Word Riddle Puzzle 50 (p. 261)

1. P   2. O
3. T   4. A
5. T   6. O

Answer: POTATO

Word Riddle Puzzle 51 (p. 262)

1. F   2. I
3. R   4. E
5. F   6. L
7. Y

Answer: FIREFLY

Word Riddle Puzzle 52 (p. 263)

1. L   2. E
3. T   4. T
5. U   6. C
7. E

Answer: LETTUCE

Rhyming Word Puzzles 53 (p. 264)

1. thin   2. pin
3. fin   4. chin
5. win   6. bin, tin

Rhyming Word Puzzles 54 (p. 265)

1. phone   2. groan, moan
3. bone   4. cone
5. loan   6. drone

Rhyming Word Puzzles 55 (p. 266)

1. comb   2. home
3. dome   4. chrome
5. Rome   6. gnome

Rhyming Word Puzzles 56 (p. 267)

1. hush   2. rush
3. slush   4. crush
5. mush   6. blush

Rhyming Word Puzzles 57 (p. 268)

1. sit   2. fit
3. hit   4. mitt
5. pit   6. knit
7. bit

Rhyming Word Puzzles 58 (p. 269)

1. fan   2. man
3. tan   4. can
5. ran   6. pan
7. Dan

Rhyming Word Puzzles 59 (p. 270)

1. game   2. tame
3. fame   4. same
5. lame   6. flame
7. name

Rhyming Word Puzzles 60 (p. 271)

1. ball   2. wall
3. hall   4. tall
5. call   6. mall
7. stall

Rhyming Word Puzzles 61 (p. 272)

1. bad lad   2. fat cat
3. tall wall   4. snug bug

10-30

Rhyming Word Puzzles 62 (p. 273)

1. big pig
2. wet pet
3. silly filly
4. mean queen

Rhyming Word Puzzles 63 (p. 274)

1. new shoe
2. small shawl
3. dumb chum
4. snack pack

Rhyming Word Puzzles 64 (p. 275)

1. sick chick
2. wild child
3. weird beard
4. dull gull

Rhyming Word Puzzles 65 (P 275)

1. grand band
2. chief thief
3. nice mice
4. fair hair

Scrambled Word Puzzles 66 (p. 276)

1. hen, cow
2. dog, cat
3. fox, ape
4. red, green
5. pear, apple

Scrambled Word Puzzles 67 (p. 277)

1. pen, pad
2. hat, sock
3. juice, milk
4. moth, ant
5. hamster, dog

Scrambled Word Puzzles 68 (p. 278)

1. Mark, Steve
2. Carol, Sharon
3. milk, butter
4. tennis, hockey
5. June, March

Scrambled Word Puzzles 69 (p. 279)

1. saw
2. war
3. pit
4. ton
5. won
6. gas

Scrambled Word Puzzles 70 (p. 280)

1. tub
2. pin
3. pig
4. dam
5. ape
6. flea

Scrambled Word Puzzles 71 (p. 281)

1. ring
2. read
3. file
4. rear
5. male
6. tale

Scrambled Word Puzzles 72 (p. 282)

1. thin
2. mane
3. wasp
4. lead
5. wolf
6. lime

Scrambled Word Puzzles 73 (p. 283)

1. name
2. vase
3. Kate
4. lose
5. Rome
6. palm

Scrambled Word Puzzles 74 (p. 284)

1. one
2. won
3. sea
4. two
5. toe

Scrambled Word Puzzles 75 (p. 285)

1. beard
2. break
3. show
4. ripe
5. blast

Scrambled Word Puzzles 76 (p. 286)

1. dream
2. search
3. bleach
4. absorb

Hidden Word Puzzles 77 (p. 287)

1. spent—pen
2. dresser—dress
3. drawer—draw
4. drink—ink

Hidden Word Puzzles 78 (p. 288)

1. team—tea
2. can dye—candy
3. butt Eric—butter
4. so far—sofa

Hidden Word Puzzles 79 (p. 288)

1. pants—ant
2. When—hen
3. was pleased—wasp
4. do very—dove

Hidden Word Puzzles 80 (p. 289)

1. mother—moth
2. cape—ape
3. plumes—plum
4. broth, Ernest—brother

Hidden Word Puzzles 81 (p. 289)

1. speak—pea
2. beetles—beet
3. be an—bean
4. car rot—carrot

Hidden Word Puzzles 82 (p. 290)

1. read in George's—reading
2. mat had—math
3. this to Ryan—history
4. germ and—German
5. cartoon—art

Hidden Clue Puzzles 83 (p. 291)

1. winter
2. wing
3. window
4. wink
5. wine
6. wind

Hidden Clue Puzzles 84 (p. 292)

1. button
2. carton
3. Washington
4. tonsils
5. tongue
6. cotton

Hidden Clue Puzzles 85 (p. 293)

1. carrot
2. carriage
3. cart
4. card
5. care
6. carfare
7. carpet
8. Carol

Hidden Clue Puzzles 86 (p. 294)

1. pants
2. plant
3. slant
4. antelope
5. lantern
6. panther
7. pant
8. antlers
9. Grant
10. antenna

Hidden Clue Puzzles 87 (p. 295)

1. bend
2. mend
3. lend
4. fender
5. tend
6. blend
7. tender
8. friend
9. fiend
10. commend

Hidden Clue Puzzles 88 (p. 296)

1. elephant—I have a trunk.
2. fish—I have scales.
3. porcupine—I have lots of needles.
4. rooster—I have a comb.
5. kangaroo—I have a pouch.